AUTISTIC CHILDREN: ONE WAY THROUGH

HUMAN HORIZONS SERIES

AUTISTIC CHILDREN: ONE WAY THROUGH

The Doucecroft School Approach

Ian B. Ashton

A CONDOR BOOK
SOUVENIR PRESS (E&A) LTD

First published 1987 by Souvenir Press (Educational & Academic) Ltd,
43 Great Russell Street, London WC1B 3PA
and simultaneously in Canada

ISBN 0 285 65040 8 casebound
ISBN 0 285 65041 6 paperback

Phototypeset by Input Typesetting Ltd., London
Printed in Great Britain by
WBC Print Ltd., Bristol

This book is dedicated to my staff who have gone through hell on earth to help these very strange and delightful children but who can switch off after a day's work; and to the parents who have gone through a worse hell but who cannot switch off; to the people who have contributed several hundred thousand pounds over the years; to the children in my care in the fond hope that, one day, even one or two of them may come to understand. It is also for John Henry Seymour who stood by in the early days, for John Jones, my Chairman of Governors, for my daughter Annie, the memory of my mother Ann, my father Bernard and, most definitely, for M.S.L. who is so important to me.

I have penned my thoughts as a way of trying to inject a little lightheartedness into what often comes over as a very dry and deadly serious subject. I hope it may also put across some of the fun I have encountered in setting up and running a school, and show some of the realities of the horrors through which some of these children can put their families. I have also tried to put over the problems of my children in a way which people who have never met them can understand.

I should like to offer my sincere thanks to the company that processed all the photographs used in this book: Alan Dench Photography, C4, Cowdray Centre, Colchester, Essex; and to the *Lancashire Evening Telegraph* of Blackburn, Lancashire, for allowing me to quote from reports printed in the paper in 1965 and 1986.

Lastly, if anyone should object to my use of the pronoun 'he' in general references to autistic children, let me assure them that it is used purely in the interests of fluency and that no chauvinism is intended.

Ian B. Ashton
December 1986

CONTENTS

The Autistic Child

My mind is a blank,
My head is a whirl,
My thoughts are all jumbled,
My speech is all mumbled.

I don't know my mother,
I don't know my father,
It's very frustrating,
My brain's not relating.

I often feel angry,
I often feel violent,
I do things so bad,
It makes people sad.

Please can you help me?
I'm not a bad person,
I need all your kindness,
I'm not really mindless.

Poem by Class 1R, St Nicholas Primary School, Tolleshunt D'Arcy, Essex, 1979. Written after one of my lectures, the decision to write taken by the children themselves.

These children expect nothing from me, so anything I can give them is a bonus, to us all.

If I don't succeed today there is always tomorrow, then the day after.

Ian B. Ashton, June, 1983, on the occasion of the opening of my new nursery, to stop the staff worrying about what I expected of them, and used as my school motto ever since.

1
WHAT IS AUTISM?

Richard is 9. He has no language at all and he seems to be totally cut off from his parents. He is a very good-looking lad and at first glance he would seem to be perfectly normal. However, it is only when you observe his very strange behaviour and witness the most incredible temper tantrums you could possibly imagine, that you begin to realise how very severely handicapped he really is. His parents have just been told by a specialist in childhood disorders that he is autistic and that the kindest thing to do would be to put him into a subnormality hospital and forget him because there is no known cause or cure for his condition.

Richard is 30. He is autistic. He has no language and seems to be cut off from the world. He is not deaf but pays no attention to anyone or anything. He was diagnosed autistic 21 years ago and, in spite of Mum's demands for help, he never received any. He went through several special schools and was excluded every time because they simply couldn't cope with his very disturbed behaviour patterns. Dad died four years ago and since then Mum has been left to cope alone. Richard neither gives nor seeks love. He has slipped through the net of a caring society.

The above quotations, seemingly without connection apart from the name, both come from the *Lancashire*

Evening Telegraph in my home town. They are about the same child and were written in 1965 and 1986.

In 1943, an American child psychiatrist called Leo Kanner referred to a group of children whom he said he had never seen before. He described them as 'autistic', a word whose stem comes from the Greek *autos*, meaning 'self', as in 'automobile' (self-propelled), or 'autobiographical' (about oneself). Kanner said that the children were non-communicating and seemed to be totally absorbed in their own world, aloof to all and sundry, including their own parents. He observed that they indulged in very strange patterns of behaviour, that they resisted all efforts on the part of therapists to intervene in their lives and were totally cut off from reality. He also stated quite categorically that the parents mostly seemed to come from professional backgrounds and that they themselves seemed to be very cold, clinical and detached.

From these observations, Kanner concluded that the parents were the cause of the 'autistic syndrome', as he called it, because he reasoned that the children had switched off from their parents as a way of trying to avoid the coldness that emanated from them. He wrote several treatises on the subject and, as the word spread, more and more doctors became involved. Unfortunately, the word autistic had also been used long before this in general psychiatry, to describe just one of the symptoms of schizophrenia, the commonest form of mental disorder. It referred to the apparently deliberate withdrawal from reality into the self-absorbing state into which many schizophrenics lapse between periods of relative calmness. It did not take long for the two disorders to become considered as very similar and closely linked, and a publication called *The Journal of Autism and Childhood Schizophrenia* was launched. This only served to entrench the idea that the two conditions were practically one and the same, and some people were of the impression that if schizophrenia could be greatly helped and even cured, then so could autism.

Many specialists studying the problem assumed it to be parentally-induced, whilst others decided it must be more complex than that, and embarked on trials to show that the cause was more likely to be chemical malfunction in the parts of the brain that controlled communication. Unfortunately, in the 1940s, even in a country as relatively advanced as the United States, very little was known about the functioning of the brain, so progress was limited; but journals churned out reams of statistics and complex charts which did nothing for the children and only served further o confuse and upset their parents. Two American scientists decided that autistic children had abnormally high levels of a particular brain chemical, and waded through years of research to prove this theory, spending an awesome amount of money before deciding that, rather than the excess chemical being the cause of autism, there was every possibility that it was a result of the handicap.

The people who really mattered were the children's parents, trying to cope with a very bewildering handicap and with no one to turn to. They were faced with trips to countless 'specialists' who churned out the same jargon but still offered no practical help at all, and were often made to feel even more desperate and more like failures by being told that they were the 'refrigerator parents' to whom Kanner had referred. Many 'experts', in the absence of knowledge, were happy enough to quote others, unaware of the problems faced by the parents.

These families must have been very cheered when, in 1963, a small group of parents in London, disillusioned by the lack of help from all quarters, founded the National Society for Autistic Children and opened up their own school for autistic children at Ealing in West London.

Until this move was made, there was nothing being done on an educational basis for autistic children in this country. Most of them were placed in State special schools, where they either caused mayhem and were excluded, to be returned home to parents who were left to manage alone as well as they could, or the quieter children were left in the corner of the classroom as the under-staffed schools applied their teachers' skills to the children whom they felt they could help. Worse still, many difficult, disturbed autistic children were left to languish in subnormality hospitals and, if they were unmanageable, were calmed down by the liberal use of chemical straitjackets.

The 1971 Mental Health Act was a tremendous boon, because it declared that 'no child is ineducable' and handed over all responsibility for every single child of school age from the Health Authorities to the Education Authorities. Unfortunately, this Act also put tremendous pressure on the Education Authorities because they simply did not have the resources to start setting up schools for severely handicapped children overnight. By this time, the National Society had established several schools—in Gravesend, Devon, Barnsley, Southport and Horsham (Sussex)—but they could not continue to do so because, as a charity, they had limited resources. Many Local Authorities set up schools within the grounds of subnormality hospitals, which was a move in the right direction, but the children were still going from a daytime school situation with relatively high staffing levels, back to the hospital wards at night. Resentment grew between medical and educational disciplines. The staff in the hospital were expected to deal with feeding and dressing, while school staff were cross if the children were late into school. Ward staff were not very happy about the long holidays given to school staff, and the whole situation was far from ideal. The National Society now has some ten schools, and other local societies have also started their own establishments, and this, coupled with the new thinking on community care, has led to less and less hospitalisation of the handicapped, including autistic children.

The National Society for Autistic Children had aims which were very straightforward: to provide education for their own children, to educate the authorities in the need to provide for such children and to educate the general public about this mystifying handicap. In the early 'sixties, Dr Mildred Creak was asked by the National Society to establish a working party to define the problem. They came up with the following list of symptoms which was at the time accepted as the definitive statement:

1 Gross and sustained impairment of emotional relationships. Aloofness or empty clinging, using people or parts of themselves impersonally. Difficulty in mixing with other children.
2 Apparent unawareness of their own identity. Confusion of personal pronouns, calling themselves 'he', 'you', 'it', and other people 'I'.
3 Preoccupation with particular objects or aspects of them without regard to their actual function.
4 Resistance to environmental change; striving to retain sameness or to restore it when disordered.
5 Abnormal perceptual responses—excessive, diminished or unpredictable response to sensory stimulation, visual or auditory avoidance. Apparent insensitivity to pain or extremes of temperature.
6 Acute, excessive or illogical anxiety—an inappropriate sense of fear or absence of fear of real danger.
7 Failure to develop any speech or the developing of echolalia (repetition of words and sounds heard), confusion of language use and failure to develop more than superficial language skills.
8 Distortion of mobility patterns; excessive movements or total immobility. Bizarre posture and ritualistic rocking, spinning, standing and walking on tip-toe, flapping and tapping constantly.
9 A background of severe retardation in which islets of normal, near-normal or exceptional function or skill may appear.

When this list first appeared, it seemed that this was

all there was to the disorder, but at the time it was all that doctors had to go on. In those days difficult-to-place children often slipped through the net and were dumped on the subnormality hospital service which had no facilities to cater for them. Unfortunately, many doctors still in practice today, in the brief time they spent touching on mental handicap in their training, would possibly have read the above list in the *Lancet* and, because of their massive workload, read nothing since. This means that there is still a tendency to decipher a child's problems on this basis alone and I have heard comments that a certain child does not 'fulfil the points on the Creak list and is therefore not autistic'. I often wonder how many parents have had their hearts filled with horror because at some stage their perfectly normal child has 'fulfilled the criteria'.

Before a suitable diagnosis can be made, it is vital to remember that *all* children pass through the stages on the list devised by the working party.

1 Any child struggles with relationships at first, choosing to flit from person to person—usually the ones who will indulge him in his needs—and only later realising that some people have more significance than others.
2 The vast majority of children confuse pronouns—which is hardly surprising. A child hears himself referred to as 'you' by other people. He hears 'Do you want a biscuit?' and next time he wants one he repeats, 'Do you want a biscuit?' because he knows that this sound pattern is linked with the biscuit tin. He calls himself 'me' as in 'he hit me' and then calls himself 'me' as in 'me want drink'.
3 Many children are attached to inanimate objects which they use inappropriately, such as carrying round pieces of blanket or other bits of rubbish, and are quite bereft when they go missing.
4 It is quite common for children to desire the same routine in life. We all need routine and, as small chil-

dren often feel insecure, they try to keep things the same to ensure that they can retain their security.

5 It is not unusual for a child to display bizarre responses to stimuli. Children are adept at apparently switching off from parents, but soon switch on again when the sweets are passed round!

6 Some children display very acute fear of normal things or people, yet will blithely step into the path of an approaching lorry or rush up to what could be a ferocious dog.

7 Whilst it is unusual for a child to fail to develop language skills, it is certainly very common for him to distort the language patterns so far away from normal that they become at best hilarious and at worst totally unintelligible. It is also common practice for a child to repeat things he hears, which is why Aunty Mary should not be criticised in front of the children! Many a family rift has been caused by children parroting their elders.

8 It is quite common to see young children indulging in all sorts of peculiar activities and movements, especially pulling strange faces and walking 'silly walks'.

Although it is true that child development involves all the above stages, autistic children do not automatically pass through them. It is more a question of being made to do so by the efforts of skilled teachers.

I suppose we could argue that everyone is born autistic, in that there is no communication at all at first. Most of us grow out of it, but, given the vast numbers of people born, it is hardly surprising that some children fail to 'come round'—about one in 2,500 by present reckoning, boys outnumbering girls by four to one. If we could understand more about how communication skills develop and get to the depths of the machinery of the brain, then perhaps we could begin to grasp what triggers off the beginnings of communication in the average person and so find a better way to make it happen in children who have failed to begin to live.

My personal definition of an autistic child is as follows:

> Anti-social or perhaps unsocialised, aggressive, self-aggressive, frustrated beyond belief, untrained toilet-wise and tablewise, unaware of others and the impact of their actions on him or of his on them, lacking in curiosity, in guile, in malice, in foresight, hindsight and even 'nowsight'. He is desperately trying to make sense of a very distorted world, a world which is so dependent on communication, a skill he has not got at his finger-tips, because his brain has failed, probably for intricate chemical reasons, to start to develop. Small wonder that he is desperate to cling to the same routine day in, day out, as a way of preserving his little bit of sanity, and small wonder that he blows a gasket when he is forced to accept any new regime in his very unhappy, disturbed world.

Many textbooks about my children are so busy pigeon-holing them into little slots in a syndrome that they forget that these are children who are still individuals, albeit strange ones, children who have their own little quirks and fancies, children with distinct personalities and funny ways, with individual levels of frustration, with varying needs to indulge obsessionally in weird behaviour patterns, and all very capable of making some progress, however small.

Puberty takes its toll, as it does of all children. The desire or need to relieve physical frustration is common—some people do, some don't. If an autistic child, lacking the language skills and thought processes needed to find more useful ways of occupying his time, finds pleasure, solace and comfort in the noble art of self-abuse it can easily become an obsession which would need limitation. But autistic children are no respecters of people or places and, if hell-bent on such things, may do so wherever and whenever—and how do you put over the concept of 'in private' to a child who cannot understand 'drink'? Adolescent acne holds no fear for these children, and why should it? You need to be aware of others' comments and opinions, their prejudices and ability to be nasty.

One could argue that my children, in their naïvety and innocence, are perhaps in some ways better off. For them no panic about growing up, no concern for jobs, marriage, taxation; no terror of nuclear war; the state of the nation causes no palpitation in their hearts. How can they panic and worry on these things when they are too busy panicking about the horrifying world around them—about terrifying creatures like people, who utter dreadful things called 'words' (which can so easily alter meaning with changing tone), and who try to persuade the children to do things they can't? Is it any wonder that they stick to their own lifestyle to a degree guaranteed to drive everyone but themselves potty, and cling to childhood routines and rituals like a limpet, as you once did? We all have problems in our lives, but at least we can communicate to help us overcome them.

Much emphasis is now being placed on the care of our children after they reach the legal education limit of nineteen years. It is not morally possible to take a child into school at, say, three years of age, and to keep him there until he is nineteen before sending him on his way to nothingness, simply because he has reached an arbitrary age beyond which he is no longer the responsibility of the Education Authority. It is obviously fervently hoped that he will need no further help after sixteen or so years in a school, but the reality is that the majority of autistic children will need help for the rest of their lives. There is only a tiny number of 'ex-autistic' people, but many can cope in sheltered accommodation, going out to work in Adult Training Centres each day; some can remain at home for as long as the parents can manage; a few, unfortunately, need hospitalisation, but most can cope very well indeed in a Life Care Centre.

The NAS started to plan more and more Life Care

Centres in the 'seventies and early 'eighties, to cater for the children who had gone through their schools, so that they could continue to live in the same sort of setting, with the same attitudes and philosophies as the schools in which they had already been shown to thrive. The idea of these centres is that the young adult can continue to develop the skills he learned in school and, hopefully, to have his physical, intellectual, emotional and social needs fulfilled. A problem arises because the law does not demand that a person aged nineteen plus has a right to be educated as it does prior to nineteen, which means the Education Authority can wash its hands of a child as he steps outside the umbrella of education. There is no law governing the Social Services who are then expected to provide funding for the child. It has been an uphill struggle to persuade the Social Services of the need to fund already trained autistic young adults in specialist centres.

Fortunately the original resistance has been broken down and several Life Care Centres are now thriving communities. Some changes in rules have meant that most of the residents are now jointly funded by the DHSS and Social Services. More places are definitely needed and places are still at a premium, but the situation has certainly much improved since the first article at the beginning of this chapter was written.

2
THE ROAD TO DOUCECROFT

My first involvement with these profoundly handicapped children came in 1965, when I read the first article quoted at the beginning of the last chapter. Richard was my aunt's next-door neighbour, and I had often seen him without ever realising that he was anything but 'that funny little kid next door'. However, it so happened that I was scheduled to write a long essay on any topic concerning education, normal or otherwise, as part of my finals at college. I immediately decided to find out what I could about autism, to distract me from thinking about French, my best subject at school, for the teaching of which I was supposedly being trained and which, having experienced two horrendous teaching practices in secondary schools in Manchester, I was dreading teaching for a living. Reasoning that no sane tutor could give me a low mark for a piece of work on a subject unknown to most, I started to find out what I could.

There was precious little information on the subject in the college, local and university libraries and, when I wrote to the National Society, they had little written information, either, because the Society was in its infancy and only had one school to use as a model. There was no way I could have visited the school in London, because I could scarcely afford my weekly dose of nicotine, let alone shoot off to the other end of Britain, and I could not expect to receive any financial aid from the college authorities for such a venture. I did find out that the Salford Education Authority had started a unit for autistic children in one of their spare classrooms, and I managed to arrange a visit to see the place. The teacher in charge seemed to be very well up on the subject and talked at length about Leo Kanner, the American child specialist who had first identified and worked with autistic children in the 'forties. She herself had been lucky enough to meet Kanner when she went to the States and had formed her own very positive ideas about working with these children.

When I asked her why autistic children needed a separate and highly specialised education, she simply answered, 'Why do blind children need special help?' She then warmed to her theme and pointed out the six or so children in her care. Every single one of the charges had his or her own personality; every one of them was like the others in that they all had the basic underlying problem of being unable to communicate; but they were all very different from each other in that they were all affected to greater or lesser degrees. There was a distinct sliding scale of severity of the handicap—very much, I suppose, as there are many degrees of handicap among Down's children.

After a short stay in this unit it became blatantly obvious to me exactly why these children needed to be educated separately from other handicapped children and also from children without handicaps: their problems were such that vast amounts of time and energy were necessary to achieve any progress at all. At a later stage in my career, I remember a visitor to my present school saying that any State school could achieve the results mentioned above, and provide the attention needed, if it had the staffing levels required. I flummoxed him totally by agreeing entirely and then sickened him by challenging him to find me such a school within the State system.

Armed with the information from this school, and with plenty of the thoughts of the teacher in charge, I returned to college to put it all on paper. A grade 'A' was awarded for my efforts, but I was then obliged to shelve the subject for a few years, while I tried to earn a meagre living and keep my sanity teaching French in a tough school in Manchester. After this I went to Turkey for a year and, on returning to England, found a job in a Primary School in Rotherham, South Yorkshire.

The head of this school decided that I had a forte for teaching children with learning difficulties. In other words, he had a class of slow learners and no one to teach them. I was given the job and, to my surprise, I loved it. In retrospect, it was quite similar in some ways to working with the children I now have in my care, because many of these slow learners were singularly bereft of basic control of the English language. After a couple of years I applied for secondment to do a full-year course in special education at Sheffield University, for I had come to the firm conclusion that there was a lot more satisfaction to be gained from working with handicapped children than there was from being insulted, harangued and even assaulted by so-called 'normal' children in a State secondary mod.

During the course of this year, instructions were issued to do a long essay on an educational topic. I immediately chose autism again and found that, after only eight years, much more information was available. Thanks to the tremendous efforts of the National Society, two or three schools were now established. Visits to them were arranged and I was made extremely welcome. I was able to find out a lot more and could feel a desire to work with these children creeping up on me. Again I saw the need to help them in specialist schools, because they had problems which needed a specialist approach and individual attention. I was probably being a little pompous in thinking that, if I ran such a school, I might perhaps change quite a few things, and I think it was at this juncture I decided to tilt for a headship. If you want things done your way you have to get in at the top. At the time, however, this seemed a pipe-dream.

While I was on the course, and gaining another 'A' mark for my thesis, I became very closely involved with the South Yorkshire Society for Autistic Children, a self-help group of parents and friends who, like the National Society, wanted more for their children than life-long incarceration in subnormality hospitals. I got to know some of the children very well and experienced a tiny bit of the hell that some of the parents were enduring every day of the week. I well remember nine-year-old David, who slept thirty minutes in twenty-four hours, and that was usually at two or three in the afternoon. He spent the rest of each day running around the house clutching his favourite toy, a load of milk bottle tops on a piece of string, screaming the place down and generally driving his parents and younger sister mad. I do not pretend to know a tenth of the torment the parents faced, but I got a good idea when I babysat for David. He put me through the mill several times over, but every time I looked after him I knew full well that it was only for an hour or so and not for a lifetime. I did feel, however, that I was giving the rest of the family a bit of normality and sanity-saving freedom, even though it was for such a short time. In desperation, David's father began taking him out for very long walks late at night in an attempt to tire him out. He reported dragging the child for miles and miles and returning exhausted at three in the morning, only to find David rushing around like a wild thing, wanting more. His father looked permanently shattered and haunted. David was rejected by several schools and his mother finished up with him at home all day and every day, as well as having a four-year-old to care for. One thing that always sticks in my mind is that they were still able to smile.

Another child I cared for occasionally was Peter. He was very much quieter than David, but if an autistic child was so defined by the list of 'points', then he was a classic case. He apparently formed no relationships at all, treating everyone with total indifference and using them to satisfy his own ends; for instance, he would drag people to things he wanted, with no realisation of the need to show any gratitude. He was totally unaware of himself, and particularly of the effect of his actions on other people. He had one word, which was 'yes'. He always emphasised the 's' at the end because at one time a well-meaning speech therapist of the old school, who thought that words at any cost were better than none at all, had tried to teach him to speak. Each time Peter sounded 'Ye', the therapist had stressed the 'sss' at the end, and Peter had picked this up, with no comprehension at all. He was obsessively drawn to a pile of pebbles in the garden and, if they were disturbed at all, he raised the roof. Whenever his mother and father took him out, he was desperate to cling to the same route; he always wanted to go in the same seat in the car and got upset when he was taken into shops in the wrong order. When his father decorated a room it took him a long time to accept it. Peter had all the funny walks you can imagine. He walked on tip-toe, sometimes backwards, and he used to pull all the strange faces under the sun, as well as having some very peculiar hand-twisting mannerisms. The ultimate experience for me with this lad came when he stripped off rapidly in a shoe shop in Sheffield and proceeded to water a shoe display. Of course he did have to choose a Saturday morning when the crowds were at their densest. I was very embarrassed and quickly pointed out to the shop staff that I would sort him out and return him to his parents.

I had lots of ideas beginning to formulate in my mind about how these children should be tackled, but could not do much about it at the time, because the first point that came to mind was that they needed very consistent handling, and I only saw David and Peter briefly and occasionally. Anything I tried to do would have to be continued by everyone who had contact with them, and I simply did not have enough time to set anything up; I had my Diploma Finals to see to and then I had to get back to working for a living.

As soon as the course was over I had to obtain a job in

Special Education. The Authority who had paid my salary for a year obviously expected me to stay in their employ for a while, so that they could benefit from my extra knowledge and new-found skills, so I was given a post at a school for ESN children, now called an MLD school (for educationally subnormal now read moderate learning difficulties). I class-taught for two terms and then persuaded the boss that I was an expert in autism. Little did either of us know that I knew nowt, as they say in Yorkshire. I was allocated a classroom and two children who were diagnosed autistic. I spent the next eighteen months with them and every day was the equivalent of World War II.

Sean was six. He spoke fluently, understanding nothing of what he said and precious little of what I said to him. He was more savage than human, as I found out when he showed me his most finely tuned skill: biting. His parents, itinerant gypsies, had left him with his grandmother who had sole charge of him. She was totally at a loss and tended to leave him to his own devices all the time, for which she could hardly be blamed. Sean tried to manipulate everyone in his world to suit his own ends. His favourite place was the cupboard, and if he was allowed to stay in there he was content. If I attempted to drag him out he went crazy, kicking and biting, screaming and yelling blue murder. I received many a visit from the girl in the next classroom because she was frequently convinced that I was being killed. Imagine, if you can, Sean's reaction to me, the first person to try to impose some sort of restriction on his little world. 'No', like 'Yes', meant absolutely nothing. 'No', accompanied by physical restraint only resulted in mind-blowing screaming. One such session lasted three quarters of an hour, but the result was 1–0 to me. He stopped and looked most amazed. I think it was the first time in his young life that he had lost a battle. It also achieved something else, because it taught me a lesson that would prove valuable in the future: if you plan to have a battle royal with a child, don't bother unless you are prepared to win; otherwise there is no point whatsoever in starting. I have developed this idea over the years as part of my philosophy, and have passed it on to my staff and to many parents.

The efforts were strenuous and worthwhile, but I was unable to stop the boss's eyes from protruding when I told him I could certainly use an assistant! This was another valuable pointer to the future and another good reason why these children require specialist education. They need very high staffing levels in schools because the effort needs to be not only intense but also prolonged. They are very different from the children normally considered to be MLD.

Sean eventually twigged the system. If I was allowed to win and he conformed, he would still be allowed, *pro tem*, to go back in the cupboard for a brief time. What he did not cotton on to was the fact that I was now in charge and was dictating the pace; I was telling him when he could and could not go in the cupboard. The next step was to get him to conform to a couple of basic rules. The first attempts to get him to sit down for his lunch were, to say the least, a farce. I started the programme by telling him to sit down. Fifty 'sit down' commands later and I revised the scheme. This time it was 'sit down' accompanied by a physical prompt. In lay terms that is best described as a shove into the chair, followed by leaning on him to give him the idea of what was expected of him. As he removed his teeth from my arm I learned another valuable lesson: being bitten is very painful! It has rarely happened to me since, although the attempt has been made many times.

The lesson to be learnt is that these children can be so unpredictable that at all times you have to be at least one step in front. I bit him back, remembering a tip from the head of the Salford school. She had tried this approach and it seemed to work. It was important not to inflict actual damage on the child: 'Well, he bit me first', would hold no water in a court of law; The legal argument would be that he was not responsible for his actions. So, rather than actually bite him with upper and lower teeth together, and exert a potential pressure of five hundred psi, I pressed my top teeth into his arm. His reaction was startling. It was not so much the pain, because normally he did not appear to be sensitive to pain; I am sure that it was the shock that someone could give him the treatment he thought only he had the right to inflict. Whatever the reason, he never tried it on again all the time I knew him.

I also learned that, in such situations, you never have the time to rationalise any of the theories of child behaviour. You act first, using what at the time seems to be the commonsense approach, and then rationalise later. If you feel, in retrospect, that it was the wrong approach, you scrap it and try something new. If it was, after consideration, the right thing to do, you store it away on paper and in your memory for a later day. Gradually Sean seemed to settle down and accept my presence, along with the rules and regulations I was trying to impose on him, and I started to look forward to each new day with this seemingly impossible challenge.

Sean's permitted free times in the cupboard gave me the opportunity to see to my other charge, Lisa. She was a pretty little girl who was the total opposite of Sean, in that she was extremely subdued all the time and chose to lie flat on her back on the classroom floor, twiddling her fingers close to her eyes. I was lying on the floor next to her just as the boss popped in. 'Don't let me disturb you,' he said, and left. I am sure he thought I was rather unorthodox in my methods.

I stared up at the apparently blank ceiling and had a quick think. What did they teach me at college about this sort of thing? Nothing. In fact, I have often asked myself if they taught me about anything at college. I reasoned that the ceiling was of no interest to Lisa at all but reckoned that a bit of colour might stimulate her. That day, after she had gone home, I covered part of the ceiling with pictures hastily gleaned from magazines and, for good measure, I added a couple of mobiles. The next day Lisa was carried in by Bert, the taxi escort. 'Nah then, lad,' he intoned, 'tha's done a reight good job wi' yon ceilin', it's just like bloody Christmas, tha knows!' Impressed though Bert was, Lisa certainly was not. She turned over on her front and seemed for all the world to be sulking madly. It was a very negative reaction, but the first reaction I had had from her.

I decided that Lisa was deriving some pleasure from the ceiling, but before I acted on that premise I first had to consider the variables. After a few cigarettes and a coffee or three, I sat down to list everything I could think of to explain why a blank ceiling could hold the interest of a child for so long. Was it lack of stimulus? Was it because she had been allowed to lie like this for years and knew no different? Was it just a habit? Did she somehow reason that, while she was there, no one would impose themselves on her? Had she found something to do which somehow felt right for her? Did she feel secure lying on a hard surface with none of the uncertainty that walking would create? The possibilities seemed endless—have another ciggy, that often helps the brain along. Have another coffee, that helps, too. Ask the colleagues, no response. I stood on a chair to peer closely at the ceiling. The tiles were not blank, they were acoustic tiles and were covered in recessed squiggles. I was trying to fathom out how on earth Lisa was able to see them from the floor when I heard the cynical old Bert say, 'Nah then, cracked up at last, owd lad? Not surprised, working in this bloody madhouse.' He muttered something about nutters and, scooping his tiny charge under his arm, carried her off.

'It's got to be worth a try,' I thought and, after a few seconds of well-intentioned vandalism, I had a tile which disappeared into my desk drawer and I went home, ready for the next day's assault on Lisa's private life. In the light of the next day I felt a bit silly as I rehearsed my lines to the boss about how this tile had amazingly fallen from the ceiling with no help at all. Now came the acid test. Bert came in and deposited Lisa on the floor. He did not have to say anything because he obviously had doubts about my sanity. I turned Lisa over onto her front and slid the tile under her nose. Nothing happened for a while and then she smiled, the first time I had ever seen her do so. Then she propped herself up on her hands and stared at the tile. A few seconds later she put her nose on it and inhaled deeply, then gave it a good lick. She seemed to be exploring the tile in every way she could think of, desperately seeking out as much information as she could.

My next step was to take the tile away to test her reaction. When it came it was pure rage. She immediately flew into a huge temper tantrum and squealed as loudly as she could. As soon as she stopped I tempted her with the tile and tried to get her to follow it and I moved it around the floor. She refused and screamed. I persisted, and finally she conceded defeat. She propped herself up and crawled along the floor towards the tile. Every time she reached it I allowed her a quick smell and a lick and then moved it further from her. Each time she protested, but the complaints became briefer and then disappeared. I would not say that it actually became a game for her, but it did cease to be a battle of wills and she seemed to be starting to understand the whole idea. I never once stopped to think that I might be entrenching her obsession even more; all I could see was that it was a means to an end to get her to move around at my prompting.

As the sessions went by I moved the tile further and higher, and one day I got Lisa to her knees. She struggled furiously, but she grabbed the tile from the shelf and actually sat up to sniff, lick and tap it. Thereafter it was quite easy to get her to move around the floor, but the best thing of all that happened was on the day when she was challenged to the full by having to get the tile from a much higher shelf. She puffed and panted and moaned and groaned, but eventually she pulled herself up to her full height and grabbed the tile. For the first recorded time in her life, she stood up. She was then six years old. From then on she never lay on the floor but proceeded to walk around like a normal child. There had never been any neurological reason why she had not walked before; she simply had not been made to do so, possibly for the usual reason of keeping the peace, and it had become a routine for her. Because she had no language or communication skills, she had never had the innate curiosity of the ordinary child, and because her lack of these skills made the world a place difficult to understand and possibly terrifying, she had never been aware of the need to explore it, choosing instead to stay in her own private little world where she could at least feel secure.

Lisa had shown that she was quite happy using her minor senses to explore her world, as are many autistic children. What they see and hear does not appear to make a lot of sense to them, so they try to compensate for these weaknesses by using the other senses. There seems to be nothing wrong with the eyes and ears, but the messages are scrambled. It was good for me that Lisa was like this, because it meant that I had a lead into a route away from her tile. I began to introduce other textures, such as materials, things which were soft or rough or smooth and which had different smells and tastes, and anything which would let her have more experience of her world.

I was going great guns with Sean and Lisa when my time was brought to an abrupt end by an accountant, of all people, who worked in the finance department of the Education Authority and who was also a town councillor. He found out about the 'experimental work' I was trying to do and persuaded the Authority that I was not 'cost effective'. The Authority agreed and I was given a classful of 'ordinary', boring (in comparison) MLD children. The Authority refused to see that autistic children really do need to be helped away from even the mainstream of special education, that they do need individual attention and that the cost is obviously going to be very high.

I felt put out to pasture when I was moved, but the experience I had gained had been very useful and I was starting to formulate my philosophy on the care, control and education of autistic children. This is a philosophy that could only be expanded and put into practice if I could find myself in control of a school. During the course at Sheffield University I had met Betty Peters, the head of a very successful school owned by the Wessex Society for Autistic Children in Christchurch on the South Coast. She had stayed in touch and I had visited her school on several occasions. She called in to visit our home one day on her travels and dropped the very large hint that the Essex Autistic Society, another self-help group of parents, planned to open a school in 1976 or 1977. I mentioned that I was interested and she replied, 'Oh, good, I'm glad you said that, because I've recommended you for the job. When they knew I was coming to visit you they just happened to mention that they would like to meet you. Can you go to Colchester on the 25th of September?'

At last it seemed that, in 1975, eight years after becoming a teacher, I had a chance of fulfilling my ambition. Although it may have seemed a little premature to assume that the job was mine before I had even found out where Colchester was on the map, I knew I was in with a fighting chance because they had actually asked to see me. When a friend mentioned to me that I had once said there was no chance of my ever moving near London because the insane pace of life in the south of England was totally unsuited to my delicate temperament, I mumbled something about not really meaning it, but the desire to fulfil my new-found ambition overrode other trivia such as the threat of king-size mortgages.

I was invited to a pub in Colchester for interview and met the committee, the Chairman of which was a delightful man called John Seymour. John asked me into the room and introduced me all round. I sat in on what was effectively a committee meeting, then John asked me to retire to the bar while they considered the situation.

There were no other applicants. A pint of Slimline Guinness later, I was recalled and offered the job. I must admit that, as the sole applicant, the thought did cross my mind that I might have been the best of a bad lot, or even the straw for the drowning man. Once offered the job, I was fully aware that, as soon as I started to run the school, I would be able to put my theories into practice and develop my own ideas of how to educate autistic children. When John mentioned a minor hitch I wondered what he might be driving at. The hitch was indeed minor—the Society did not actually have a building purchased, they only had one in mind, in Chelmsford, the county town of Essex. My very first task on the 6th January, 1977, would be to arrange inspection of this building.

3
ALL HANDS TO THE PUMP

The architect's verdict was delivered with cynical detachment. John Finch is a reputable man in his field and is now a good friend of the Society. I had no reason whatsoever to doubt his word but was, to say the least, dismayed as he calmly said, 'Tell you what, old boy, just concentrate on the top floor because in a few years' time that is all that you or anyone else will see of this place above the ground.' The Towers, quickly nicknamed 'Fawlty Towers', was a Victorian heap waving a fond farewell as it slowly but surely sank into the tip upon which it had been built in 1872. HM Inspector of Schools was equally direct. 'I wouldn't want a child of mine to attend school in this building,' he said. In other words, there was no way that he would give permission for Local Authorities to send children to an independent school in this dreadful place. The seal of total disapproval was complete when the Fire Officer gave his opinion that 'the best way to avoid a fire in this rat-trap would be to burn it down and start again'. He then offered to supply the matches. The Society was left with no option but to agree with me that its initial choice of property was perhaps slightly less than ideal.

After the usual exclamations of shock and despair, I was asked to search for another property. Some were too big, some too small, some superb but far too pricey, whilst some were almost derelict. Others were ideal but so far from normal lines of communication that they would have disappeared under the first signs of snow, and staff would have found it impossible to get to and from work. I asked every estate agent in Essex to put me on their mailing lists, an exercise which served little purpose apart from giving me plenty of paper to burn during the cold months of winter. I suggested to the committee that, instead of asking for information merely on large properties, we should be setting ourselves a target for the maximum price we could manage. The very small group of parents who had started the Society a couple of years before had raised the startling total of £25,000, in itself a major feat. Tony Boobier who, single-handed, had gone out talking to anyone who would listen, had raised the bulk of this himself and had also suffered at the hands of some so-called 'experts'. He was accused in writing, and I have seen it, of being 'publicity-mad', and on one occasion the suggestion was made that 'one should keep one's illness in one's family'. For anyone to make such comments about a father who devoted a large chunk of his life to keeping his son out of subnormality hospitals for ever and a day, was a travesty and a tragedy.

The above comments will perhaps give some idea of the difficulties I felt might arise in persuading the Authorities to send children and pay for them at our proposed new school. I felt all along that there was a strong undercurrent of hostility. This surfaced when I was misquoted in the press. A reporter, preparing a short article for the local paper, asked me how many children I envisaged being able to take into the school. Off the top, I told him twelve, the type-setter put in '120' as a heading, and I received an amazing letter from the then Director of Education, on the lines of, how dared I get the press to print the fact that the County Council was prepared to fund so many children in an independent school? My first reaction to this letter was 'Gulp!' and then I hastily wrote back explaining that this was merely a typographical error; at the same time I requested an urgent meeting with the Authority so that we could establish a sensible base-line to work from. The meeting was set up and John Seymour and I took ourselves to the Education Offices.

The meeting was quite heated and voices started to be raised. The main contention from the Authority's point of view was that there were no autistic children in the county (it must have been the fresh air from the sea!). I mentioned the request from the Secretary of State, some time earlier, for details of numbers of autistic children in each Authority's care, and suggested that something had turned up. I was then shown a minute from an Education Committee meeting that stated there were fifty-four children, aged between five and sixteen, who had severe communication problems but were to be catered for in the new communication unit to be established in Chelmsford.

I felt that this initial reluctance on the Authority's part was another bit of creative accountancy, similar to the verdict of 'lack of cost-effectiveness' inflicted on me a few months earlier, and in the same vein as the reports we read that our roads are in good order, when cars are disappearing into potholes every day of the week. An officer's statement, that they had been told to prune the Education budget by several million pounds that year, only served to back up this idea. I was asked how we could expect the Authority to find further cash to fund children with us when such cuts had been ordered.

John pointed out the tremendous cost of keeping a child in long-term subnormality hospital for the rest of his or her days, and the high cost of psychiatric care for parents when they cracked up. We presented a paper showing our projected costings and pointed out that we were relatively cheap, that our fees were lower than many other independent special schools, that we would offer a service that parents were clamouring for, and that there were enough children in the county diagnosed as autistic to fill the proposed school over and over again. These were children who had been seen by the leading lights of the handicapped world at such eminent hospitals as the Maudsley and the Institute of Psychiatry in London.

We were able to demonstrate that there would be no capital costs for the Authority. We would be buying the building and supplying all the equipment; we would be totally responsible for the upkeep of the property and, if the roof dropped in, that was down to us. We were also able to point out that HM Inspectorate and the DES were in favour of the project. Moreover, we had a precedent: the National Society and other local Society schools. It was then disclosed that some Essex autistic children were, in fact, already attending the National Society school in London, which meant that the Authority actually did accept that there was such a thing as autism.

Eventually the promise was made that the school would be considered by the Authority, but it would have to be seen in action before a decision could be made as to whether they would be able to send children there. This presented a real poser, because the school needed children to function but could not get them until it was functioning—which, to say the least, put us in a cleft stick. We left the meeting somewhat disillusioned and tried to fathom a way round this obstacle.

At the next committee meeting we took a decision, or rather made an act of faith. We asked the bank manager, the custodian of our £25,000, to be a governor of the proposed school. He accepted, and we then asked our new governor for a loan of a further £25,000, which was the maximum we felt we could cope with. The loan was swiftly arranged and we set off in hot pursuit of every property in the county costing around £50,000.

One day, bored senseless with repeated trips along the motorway from Chelmsford, where I lived, to Colchester, where the secretary lived, I decided to make a detour through a little town called Kelvedon. And there, on a beautiful summer day in June 1976, I screeched to a halt outside a fine Georgian house with a 'For Sale' sign at the front. It was lunch-time and the only thing that moved was the magnolia tree by the porch. Something told me that this was the place for us and I rang the selling agents.

The house had been a home for sixteen maladjusted boys, now called EBD (for emotionally and behaviourally disturbed), and had been closed by the Social Services who used to run it. It was a snip in those days at £42,500, and we would still have a few thousand left for renovations, alterations and equipment. A few calls to the committee resulted in a meeting at the house that night and everyone was sold on the place.

We put in a bid which was promptly passed by a local builder. He found out that we were his rivals and invited us to discuss things at his office. He did not want the house, he explained, he wanted the land at the rear for building. If we were prepared to opt out of the race, he would buy the lot and sell us the house, minus a portion of land. Having accepted that he was too wealthy to compete with, we discussed the question of boundaries and left, satisfied that we were doing the right thing. A few weeks later the Society's solicitor, an extremely kind man called John Jones, now Chairman of the school governors, called to say that contracts were complete and would be finalised on 23rd February, 1977. The house is called 'Doucecroft', which is very significant, because 'douce' is French for 'sweet' and 'croft' means 'dwelling place', so the whole name, roughly translated, means 'home, sweet home'. It could not be more appropriate.

During the long wait to find and secure the building, I was kept extremely busy trying to raise money. I had a definite incentive to do so, because funds were mostly committed to the property purchase and there was no endless source of money pouring in to help keep me and my family. At this stage, now that we were so near the target, it was vital to keep support flowing in. As a registered charity we had a useful advantage: there was no tax to pay on any interest earned from banks. Mind you, that is just about the only help from the State that a charity such as ours can expect. I therefore embarked on a career of public speaking. I had never given a lecture in my life and was still very conscious of my northern accent;

moreover, since the school was not yet open, it was rather hard to talk about it.

The first lecture that I was invited to give was to the local Round Table. I have found over the years that Tablers are very silly, serious, kind, generous, concerned, involved and committed people, all at the same time. The guys I spoke to were just that. They met regularly to swap pleasantries, jokes, information and to share their concern for others, especially the less fortunate or deprived. As I began to speak their rowdiness subsided and, when I launched into a description of the problems of our children, I was gratified to see forty men listening intently. As they left, there were many counting their blessings and some were visibly shocked. That summer they held a fair for the school and presented us with a fat cheque for £3,000 to buy all the kitchen equipment that we would need. Inspired by their response, I took on more lectures and was prepared to talk to anyone who was ready to listen.

I lectured to a multitude of groups. Very frequently the people who are given the job of speakers' secretary find themselves with a thankless task. They are often desperate to come up with a speaker and so I found myself in demand. Word also gets around by word of mouth when Mary, who belongs to one group, mentions your name to Margaret in another group, and the number of lectures doubles rapidly. I was actually asked what my fee was, but I always said that if the group would make a donation to the funds there would be no fee. Some of the groups I have spoken to have been extremely generous; only a tiny handful have donated just enough to cover my petrol money and only one group failed to give us anything at all. I think that the vast majority of people hearing about my children go home thanking their God and mine that they have normal children.

Other attempts at fund raising were disastrous. On taking the post of Headteacher elect, the first job the committee gave me was to finish organising a concert they had started to plan. When they said 'started to plan', they meant that the artistes were booked to appear free. All I had to do was arrange publicity, book a hall, get the tickets printed and generally deal with other such mundane and trifling details! All the organisation went well, including the distribution of three hundred posters around town. The only thing that failed was a matter that cried out for consideration: we had only sold two, yes two tickets, four days before the event! I was in a state of total panic because I was convinced that the whole disaster would reflect very badly on my skills as an organiser. In desperation I rang the Chairman. He told me to give tickets away and said that he would organise the covering of any shortfall. In the event we gave away five hundred and ninety-eight tickets, had a fabulous concert, made up a bit of leeway with a raffle at half-time and learned a valuable lesson: fund raising is hard work and the best way to do it is by a method that brings in the maximum money with the least effort in the shortest possible time.

With this lesson firmly fixed in my mind, I wrote to HMSO and asked for the London Diplomatic List. It always amazes me that anyone, including potential terrorists, can get their hands on such a document, which lists the name of every embassy, its address and the names of all the diplomats who work there. The object of my exercise was not to bomb but to blitz—with requests for cash. Everyone has read of the fabled wealth of the Arabs, so I wrote to every single Arab set-up in the book. I reckoned that they had money mountains like the EEC has food mountains and I was convinced I was on to a winner. It only needed a smallish donation from a few and we would be laughing, so it is easy to imagine how my hopes soared when I received a letter from the Royal Saudi Arabian Embassy. I was invited to go to Belgrave Square to speak to the Ambassador himself. On arriving, I was ushered into an ante-room bigger than my house and sat up to my knees in priceless Persian carpet. I began to dream of harems and eunuchs and the like, and was then summoned to the Sanctum Sanctorum. There I received what can only be described as a culture shock. I had expected to see the Big Man dressed in full desert gear and wearing a flowing head-dress. Instead he wore a lounge suit and smoked Players No 6. He offered me coffee and again I was shattered. Convinced that I would be offered genuine Turkish-style coffee, I said 'Yes please', only to be rewarded with a cup of 'instant' Nescafé and the time-honoured phrase, 'God, I hate this rubbish!' I was given no promise of help and left dismayed, but I am sure that if I was reinvited now with the fund-raising skills I have developed since then, he would be left begging me to take his money.

Ony day early in my career I was recommended to write to the Lord-Lieutenant of the County to see if there was any way in which he could help. I was invited to speak to him at his home, one of the most superb buildings in the whole of Essex. A real-life Jeeves answered my knock and I was ushered into the study, one wall of which was a bookshelf crammed with valuable first editions. He stood chatting for a while as we waited for the Lord-Lieutenant, and pointed out the West Wing where 'Henry and Ann slept' and, 'Her Majesty sleeps there when she is visiting the county'. When Sir John came in from his morning shoot he showed tremendous interest in the school and our plans for it. He made a healthy donation and promised to contact the Authority to put his point of view. To demonstrate his confidence, he made me promise to invite him to perform the opening ceremony whenever it was to be. Confidence indeed, perhaps more than I had myself, because we still had no commitment from the Education Authority to put children forward.

As soon as the building was purchased I began to get a stream of 'phone calls from parents desperate to get their children into the school. I had to tell them all to apply for placement through the Local Authority, because they would have to pay the fees. I had already been apprised of a situation where the Head of one proposed school had told lots of parents of physically handicapped children that they could have a place, and that all they had to do was get the Authority to agree to pay the fees. It turned out that the Authority had never even heard of the school and had no idea at all of the facilities it had to offer. That particular school was destined never to open. I met many parents over the months and heard the same story over and over: the anxiety, the heartache, the dreadfully fraught situation where the child was totally disruptive; or the tales of children who did nothing all day but rock and twiddle with useless objects. There were stories of children who had appeared quite normal for about the first eighteen months of their lives and had then seemed to switch off, of children who were unbelievably different from the other children in the street, or from how their siblings had been.

I had some idea of how these parents coped or failed to cope because, for my first three months in Essex, I had in fact been in digs with an autistic family. Sally was one of the most incredibly difficult eleven-year-olds I had ever seen. At one stage in her life, when her mother had been told for the umpteenth time that she was the cause of Sally's problems, Barbara had herself been taken into psychiatric hospital where she challenged the psychiatrists and other 'experts' to prove her, as they had said, unbalanced. After two weeks in this place, she told me, there were six doctors sitting at the foot of her bed and they told her that, apart from suffering from incredible stress because she had Sally to deal with, she was perfectly normal. Barbara told me that she screamed at them to do something, but still no help came. Sally had already been excluded from several local schools because she was deemed to be unmanageable. The next day Barbara took Sally to the Social Services and told them that she could no longer cope with her and that, unless they did something to help her, Sally would be left with them. She was challenged to do just that, but they had picked on a woman at the end of her tether. 'OK, Sal, do your worst,' she said, and walked out. Within minutes someone brought Sally home from an almost demolished Social Services office and promised that a case conference would be held very soon. It was, and two weeks later Sally was placed in a National Society school that had a vacancy. What a tragedy that the family had to reach such a desperate level before our so-called caring agencies were forced to get involved, and what a tragedy also that, once they did, they found it so easy.

One amusing incident from those days sticks in my mind. I invited one family to tea at our house and along they came with Jimmy, who was to become one of our first pupils. Jimmy shot straight into the garden and seized my baby daughter's toy radio. It was one of those infuriating gadgets that plays a tune until it winds down, and you cannot switch the damn' thing off. I was secretly pleased, because visitors took great delight in winding it up fully and seeing me gnash my teeth as 'Raindrops keep falling on my head' was played for the millionth time. As it was described by the makers as indestructible, I returned it to them, only to have them deny that a child could have wreaked such havoc. A thirty-ton lorry, yes; a child? No, no, no. A further letter from me describing the remarkable demolition skills of some autistic children resulted in a handsome donation to the funds and a new radio which played 'My grandfather's clock'!

I do not know if the Lord-Lieutenant had spoken to anybody, or if the Education Officers had decided that Doucecroft was a good idea after all, but either way, two days after completion I was asked to consider a total of nine children. I was given the keys and had to draw up a plan of campaign to get the place sorted out. The architect had given the building a good going-over, HMI had stated that he was well impressed and the Fire Officer had told me exactly what was needed in the way of a fire system. A good firm was contacted and they started work three days later; you have never in your life seen so many cables and other bits and bobs lying around.

I set myself a deadline of 2nd May, 1977, for the first intake of children. My list of work seemed endless: decorate, find equipment, find the staff, see to the kitchens and services, like water and gas. I decided that the only way to get organised was to do everything concurrently. I advertised for staff and within a week I had a total of three hundred and twenty-seven applicants. Amazingly enough there were only two men amongst the whole lot. Interviews were carried out in extreme conditions. The shortage of furniture meant that interviewees had to sit on old boxes and, in one case, on the floor because the box collapsed, and on most occasions this meant having to search for a box amongst the piles of junk. As each interviewee was appointed she was given a starting date of 18th April; if she was free then she was given the opportunity to start before and to help me with the decorating.

Berger paints were kind enough to donate more than thirty gallons of brilliant white emulsion and gloss and I got stuck in. Thirty-one ceilings needed painting and I very quickly became depressed, so I did the only thing possible and went to the local for a pint. Being a rural area, Kelvedon has lots of farmers and three of them were in the pub having a conversation about crop spraying. This prompted my tired brain, so as soon as I returned to school, I filled up a garden spray with white emulsion and attacked the job with gusto. Covered in drips though I was, I had dealt with eighteen ceilings by 5.00 pm—the previous day I had completed three in the same period.

If my painting technique left much to be desired, it paled to nothingness compared with the performance put up by the local Girl Guide troop. Because of the limitations of their height and therefore their reach, I was a little dubious of this generous offer of help, but it would have been churlish to refuse and I hoped that other local people, inspired by these young ladies, might leap into action. At first, the sight of said young ladies raring to go brought a feeling of delight to my heart. All this work for them and thus not for me, I thought. But as the day wore on I began to develop a feeling of acute panic. They sang 'I love to go a wandering' in time to their two-handed swings of brushes overloaded with precious emulsion and the wet slap-slap of brushes on walls was only interrupted by the scurrying of tiny feet rushing for the next dip. They were doing a fantastic job, their energy was boundless and frightening and resulted in a head-to-foot anointing with brilliant white emulsion. This was easily washed off, but you should have seen the mess they made with the gloss. Being a bit low on white spirit, I considered it more prudent to clean the brushes that these girls had purloined from home, because the thought of a posse of angry dads coming to lynch me did not appeal. Seriously, those girls saved me a tremendous amount of work and the Society a lot of money, and I am forever grateful.

As the organisation went ahead it became very obvious that some rather major changes were needed. Doucecroft was built in 1618 and I can feel quite confident when I say that the builders probably did not have it in mind for the place to become a school. Mind you, I would have expected the people who installed the first heating system, at some stage in the 1950s, to have realised that Britain was slowly heading towards the next ice-age, but they had installed a system that was totally and utterly inadequate. I think that the warden of the children's home had used open fires to boost the temperature, but we could not follow suit because very few autistic children have any sense of danger.

As ever, it was necessary to get the job done as cheaply as possible. A local plumber was recommended to me; he offered a very fair price for a completely new system and suggested that if I were to be his labourer the price could be reduced ever further. Then, with a flash of inspiration, he responded to my acceptance of even more work by trying to get the price even lower. He told me that a group of diddycoys, itinerant gypsies, who were camping locally, would be quite happy to remove the existing three-inch system and its six radiators free of charge, so long as they got the scrap-metal for their efforts.

They turned up the following morning full of silent purpose and seemed to have an IQ of 150—between the six of them. They had had their brief from the plumber and, with a 'Top o' the morning to you, sir', they got stuck in. They were big blokes so I thought it prudent not to mention the fact that they were about to start in the only room that did not need re-decoration. It soon became clear that, big as they were, sheer muscle-power alone was of little value and in came the dreaded oxy-acetylene torch. The flames soon had the desired effect, but not just on the pipework. The wallpaper, too, was burning and I had visions of my lovely timber-framed career going for a burton. However, the combined size and weight of six Irish tinkers was enough to persuade me to pretend that they knew what they were doing, so I remained silent.

The superficial damage that they had caused was soon sorted out when, two minutes later, as the flame bit through the pipe, a torrent of filthy, stinking heating system water cascaded all over the floor, drenching the smouldering wallpaper as it went. The idiots had failed to drain the sytem before they started. The torch wielder raised an eyebrow in silent communication with his thick friends. He doused his flame; the tools and gas bottles, along with the radiators and other bits, were assembled with funereal dignity, and they slowly marched out of the door, 'Torchy' touching his forelock and promising to return after lunch. There is no need to add that they did not. Leaving one very unhappy headteacher weeping on the floor amidst the flood.

I took the philosophical view that nothing worse could happen and, picking up a large hammer, got on with the job. Three days later twenty-nine new slimline radiators adorned the walls and the plumber was left to get on with the pipework. The plumber also arranged for a scrap-metal merchant to come in and we received £120 for the remaining scrap.

Not all the DIY efforts were to cause such hassle. I persuaded one of our prospective dads to beg, steal or borrow as much in the way of wire, switches, cable clips and light fittings as possible from his employer, the CEGB, and, with the help of an amateur electrician friend, we rewired the whole lighting system in eight days flat. When we saw the condition of the old cables we were more than pleased that we had taken the trouble because it was a potential death trap. Miraculously, when we switched the mains on everything worked perfectly first time. Dick Willson had given up a week of his annual holiday and refused point blank to take a penny. It is thanks to him and a host of other very kind, concerned people that Doucecroft has survived and will continue to do so.

One limitation to my skills was the manufacture of furniture, so a hastily erected sign was put outside the front door. This brought a tremendous response in the way of all sorts of goods and 'not so goods'. The majority of the stuff was either usable or saleable, with a few items, quite frankly, beyond their best. A gallon of paraffin disposed of these on a huge bonfire, along with vast quantities of rubbish accumulated from my labours. We were given enough in the way of beds, tables, chairs and other furniture at least to give us a start and, during those weeks, we also received a steady flow of gifts and goods, such as home-made jam and other produce.

My new team of staff, comprising four classroom assistants, one teacher, two night staff, a cook, secretary and cleaner, started just two weeks before the first intake of five children. Without hesitation they set about scrubbing floors, moving heavy furniture, putting up curtains and laying carpet. We had many discussions about the problems that these children might present and quickly decided that speculation was a waste of time. Many of the girls had read the well-known texts on autistic children but were obviously convinced that it would be pointless to anticipate anything without meeting the actual children. So, instead of continuing to discuss the, as then, unknown children we retired to the George each lunchtime to get to know the locals and each other a little better. The most moving moment came when I saw eight ladies pushing a door to and fro, while another held the saw still, in a disastrous attempt to shorten the door. However, this showed that they had a sense of humour, which was to prove extremely useful. They had all entered a very strange world—one day happily unemployed or ensconced in a cosy office, and the next thrown into a place which, unbeknown to everyone at the time, was about to erupt into what could only be described as a total disaster area: our deadline day of Monday, 2nd May, 1977.

4
OUR FIRST CHILDREN

After all the preparation, hassle, laughs and panic, the first day began calmly enough. The staff did not know what to expect and I was loath to say anything to spoil their mood of confident tranquillity. This mood was shattered soon enough at 9.15 am, as our first pupil arrived by taxi. The driver fell from the car with blood oozing from a deep scratch on his neck and, with great self-restraint, delivered his charge into the school before driving off at high speed, back to the relative sanity of collecting fares in London traffic. J.C., as we fondly christened him from his initials, went straight into the toilet and locked himself in. No amount of persuasion would entice him out, so a more subtle approach was called for. I kicked the door in just in time to see his clothes being pushed into the toilet. J.C. then pulled the chain. I think he was trying to flush them away in the fond hope that he would follow them and escape from this dreadful place, which he possibly suspected was going to ask things of him, things he would be unable to do or understand.

That same morning produced further dramas as the other children arrived. William was totally out of control as he dragged me by the hair onto the floor. He was pouring forth his entire vocabulary of twenty-five words (all reported on his Special Education forms, and all sounding like 'mama'). He crashed around the school like a man possessed by Satan. As my staff stood and stared he then began to hammer his forehead against the wall with his full force. William was already fourteen years old and had the strength of thirty men.

Vicky crossed the threshold and wet and soiled herself within minutes. She also made a loud sort of glug-glugging noise in her throat, which we soon found she would do every single time she was upset. Jimmy was the quietest and easiest to manage at the time, because he simply stood on the spot and stamped his feet, shouting 'Ah!' at the top of his voice. He was still in nappies at the age of six. Edwin did not walk into school, he flew. He hurled himself into a corner and proceeded to scream, yelling and banging his head on the wall, at the same time biting himself viciously on his wrist. It was obviously going to be a pitched battle as the staff took breath and tried to make some sense of what was happening to them. The kettle was our saviour and I praised Sir Walter Raleigh for discovering tobacco. Interestingly enough, nine of those initial staff were smokers and certainly proved this that morning.

Somehow we survived until what we had previously decided would be playtime, and the children were allowed out into the garden. Because the school was so new we had precious little playground equipment but this did not deter the children. The headbangers carried on doing just that, Vicky showed us just how much grass and leaves she could scavenge in a very short time and Jimmy continued to stamp his feet. The staff tried valiantly to stop some of the more horrendous self-attacks, but when you have precious little experience of these particular children, do not know your way around the building, hardly know your colleagues and feel like running away, there is not a lot you can do apart from trust your own judgement and hope that whatever you try will work.

We persevered until lunch-time and saw the cook, who had heard the screams from afar all morning, obviously trying to keep a brave face; but nothing could have given her any warning of what to expect in her baptism of fire.

The five children were brought into the dining-room with six staff. The teacher, the four classroom assistants and I sat them down, or rather tried to sit them down, and served up the lunch. Edwin screamed and his food was removed. The very second he stopped, his meal was replaced and he was allowed to eat. The moment he started screaming again it was removed. This went on throughout the session because we knew he liked food, according to his SE forms, but we were determined that there was to be no food offered when he was being unacceptable.

This has always been one of my contentions: if a child is ever allowed to have something nice or something he particularly wants when he is being objectionable, then his bad behaviour is not only being reinforced, it is being severely ingrained and it will prove the devil's own job to eliminate. With Edwin we had at least fifty removals and re-offerings in that one session, but in the end he finished on a happy note by having an empty plate and then he was doubly rewarded with a sweet, a kiss and a cuddle. He loved the sweet but was not overly keen on the kissing.

During the same meal Vicky sat quietly enough, but insisted on trying to eat with her fingers. We removed the knife and fork because we felt she could not manage them, and gave her a spoon. She was our youngest at five-and-a-half, and we felt that it was still early days. We thought that the refinements of etiquette could be delayed until we had persuaded her of the need to stay in her place and eat without playing with food. She was allowed to continue to eat with her fingers, so long as she did not mash the food around, and a member of staff put a spoon in her hand and held it there, with her hand cupped firmly over the child's. Every third mouthful of food that went in by hand had to be followed by a spoonful. The first time this was done she glug-glugged and the plate was taken away. The noise stopped immediately and the plate was returned, then the routine of three to one was done again and again, and we got her through the meal.

J.C. was trying all the time to get down from the table, but his good point was that he knew how to handle his cutlery, so his meal went down well. As the only verbal child in the room, he was saying, 'Go 'ome,' every time he was told to sit down. He bit himself a couple of times and, for good measure, slapped his face now and again. We had the whip-hand because he, too, enjoyed his food and his plate, like Edwin's, was removed each time he kicked up. He finished eating in a relatively calm manner and was rewarded with seconds. Jimmy ate perfectly and has never done anything else.

The most remarkable eating session was William's. He had two staff members with him at all times to prevent or try to limit his aggression. To our amazement, he sat down, picked up his knife and fork and waited patiently for his food. Then he hit us with both barrels. Down went his food like a commuter's lunch in a Wimpy bar and then, with one rapid contraction of his stomach muscles, back it came onto his plate and only a super-rapid intervention on my part stopped it going down for a second time. As soon as I interfered he went absolutely crazy and tried to wrestle me to the floor for the second time that day. This time I was too quick for him and was able to pin *him* to the floor instead. At that moment I said something which was to become an unwritten code between us from then on. I simply said, 'One of you,' and a colleague joined in. Ever since, we have used this formula, or, in some cases, 'Three of you,' or even more. Between us we were able to hold him until he calmed down, which took a good fifteen minutes.

It is surprising how often over the years we have been able to develop approaches to the children's problems by trial and error. It is not the easiest job in the world to read a book and then apply what you have read to a child. In fact, if you do that, you should not be surprised if it fails. Everything I have written about individual children illustrates this. I would never apply a blanket statement to these children by saying that if you do this, the result will be that. Almost everything we have achieved with our children has been on a 'try it and see' basis. If it fails, file it away in case it may work with another child, if it works do not knock it. As your experience grows you remember various approaches more easily and you grow in confidence in the way in which you handle the children. Another spin-off from this growth of confidence is that new children seem to feel it and it becomes much easier to help them.

The afternoon of Day One flew by and, by four o'clock, we had some semblance of a routine. The children's cases had been unpacked (by the children) and their toiletry bags and contents were sorted out in the bathrooms. We had had many outbursts from William and Edwin. Edwin's were easier to cope with because all his aggression was inflicted on himself, but William's was also inflicted on others. This made him a potential danger to the other children as well as to staff and it was obvious that there were difficult times ahead. I decided that isolation was the first thing to try, so every time he kicked up he was to be given one chance to stop and then he was to be put into the room we had prepared for the purpose. It was simply an empty room, with smooth walls and no projecting corners, in which he could do no more damage then he was doing in front of everyone. The theory was straightforward enough: if he was used to getting attention by hurting himself and other people, it was worth trying to remove him from his audience.

I am certain that this approach had never been tried in any of the ten schools that William had already attended, because the very first time he went in there he stopped within minutes. He was allowed out the second he finished and was praised for stopping. This established the next rule: always praise the child when he stops doing something wrong. This may appear to some to be plain common sense, but I argue that, although we are always ready to praise a child for doing something right, we tend to forget that, if he stops doing something wrong, he is in fact doing something right, and that this needs to be reinforced.

Tea-time was still a nightmare, but not quite so bad as lunch had been. The children seemed to be calming down a little, and we got through tea in relative harmony. We also learned another very important lesson. Vicky started to be very stubborn about keeping quiet and was having her food removed constantly. The girl working with her was struggling along bravely when one of her colleagues decided to help. With an adult each side of her Vicky went crazy, but calmed down considerably as soon as the second person backed off. The child could barely cope with one person telling her what to do, but two people were simply more than she could take. The rule for all time was thus written: you never get involved in a colleague's problems unless you are asked to do so.

The next hurdle was to get through bathtime. J.C. enjoyed his and gave us a pointer to the future that we could use this as a reward for things done well or for bad things stopped. Jimmy was very much 'take it or leave it', but we found that his greatest joy in life was to be tickled. This later proved to be very instrumental in getting him to talk. Edwin relaxed a little in the bath and showed a liking for nursery rhymes. The girl working with him sang the beginning of several rhymes and he sang the rest in a beautifully clear voice. He had no spontaneous language at the time but obviously loved music, which was yet another pointer to the future activities that we could plan. William proved to be a real pest in the bath. At fourteen he was well aware of the pleasure to be gained from self-stimulation and he was hell-bent on masturbation. When we attempted to remove him to a more private place, he went crazy for the umpteenth time that day. I had to isolate him again, but as soon as he calmed down I pushed him towards the toilet instead of the bathroom, and there he completed the task in hand.

When he came out he seemed to much more peaceful and finished getting ready for bed.

By the time the new night staff came in to work at ten to eight, the five children were in bed and apparently sound asleep. The four classroom assistants, with the teacher who had stayed behind, walked out reeling, and I wondered if they would all turn up the following day or if they would be unable to recover from the obvious state of shock in which they found themselves. I stayed to talk to the night staff, to go through the record book with them to discuss the things we had discovered about the children, and to wish them luck on their first night. They had a twelve-hour shift to get through, which was a long time for two relative strangers to be together. I made sure that they had my 'phone number and drove home in a daze, wondering what the hell I had let myself in for.

The 'phone did not ring that night, and I returned to school at seven o'clock the next morning. I had not expected the night staff to have an easy time of it, but I was unprepared for what I found. They were both in a state of nervous exhaustion and looked extremely mutinous. We had got through the first day roughly in one piece and knew that we had been through the mill, but if we had had a day, the night staff had had a night and a half. Only Jimmy had slept through the night—the other four had caused chaos. They had all soiled themselves and had all liberally fouled their beds and bedrooms. Vicky had covered herself in her own excrement and had eaten large quantities of same. J.C. had not gone so far, but had executed some beautiful patterns on the windows. He had also removed the door knob and hidden it, more of which I shall tell you later. Edwin had used his suitcase as a toilet and there was mess in it, on it, under it and all around it. William had spent half the night masturbating and the other half wetting, soiling, smearing and daubing the walls, curtains, floors and himself.

I have always prided myself on being a positive thinker, and was quick to point out to the night staff that they had four horror stories but had only glossed over their twenty per cent success rate. Jimmy had not put a foot wrong, apart from having a wet bed, for which a child should never be sanctioned unless he has done it on purpose. 'You're right', they mumbled, eyes half-closed with fatigue. When I asked if they would be back that night they both assured me that it would need a lot more than they had had to put them off. 'Now there's positive thinking,' I said. 'Well done!'

This incident gave me two valuable lessons in one. Firstly, it is not enough to be a positive thinker; you have to let other people see it clearly so that they will begin to think on the same lines. Secondly, I realised that it was vital for me to make sure that I looked for things that I could praise in what my staff did and said. All of us need recognition of what we do well; that way we do the same again, feel good about things and are much more able to take any criticism that has to come our way.

As well as trying to sort out the five children I was also still heavily involved in giving lectures, in organising further equipment and showing visitors round. The school attracted a great deal of interest, the most significant of which was a visit by a crew from the local ITV station. They came on the Thursday morning of the first week and filmed the children, followed by an interview with me. The interviewer said that he would first ask me questions in a dummy run, to get me used to the cameras and so that I would not be caught out by anything unexpected. He then said he was ready to film; I should pretend I had not already answered his questions and I must not start each answer with the word 'well'. As he asked his first question with the camera rolling, I started off, 'Well . . .' At this juncture a crash of breaking glass obliged me to leave the interview, to find that William had stuck his foot through a window. Medical treatment was needed, so I had to abandon the TV men and shoot off to the doctor. Upon my return the first question the reporter asked was whether it was always like this. After checking that the camera was not running, I answered, 'I bl - - - - hope not'.

Little did I know then that things were to remain exactly like this for some time to come. After lunch on the first Friday, when all the children had gone home to their families for the weekend, we had our first formal staff meeting, at which we discussed what we had learnt and where we were going to go. It was obvious that all our children, whatever the cause of their problem, were presenting mostly severe behaviour disorders. It is not necessarily a consequence of being autistic that a child is so disordered, but years of frustration at the inability to communicate clearly leave the child in a state of torment and panic, and he shows this as best he can by becoming, like a small baby, easily angered and difficult to control. We knew, as I had found from previous experience, that each autistic child needed totally individual treatment. Without even discussing things in detail, we had already sorted out several programmes of behaviour modification by using a totally trial-and-error approach, as with Vicky's eating patterns and William's masturbation.

We also realised the great importance of communicating with each other about all aspects of the work and of trying to learn self-criticism. I asked if anyone felt that she had made any obvious mistakes, and the girl who had stuck her oar in with Vicky at tea-time admitted that she had been wrong. After this admission other people began to talk about their own errors. One girl said she felt she had done the wrong thing when she had told Edwin off from the other side of the playground. She realised that her voice had had little impact on him and that she should have gone to the child instead. Someone else realised that when she told J.C. to come to her, she should have stood her ground until he did, but instead she had let it go.

It was obviously rather difficult for people to admit that they could see where they had gone wrong, but as soon as this self-pulling-to-pieces was over I asked everyone to mention a success. In that hell-on-earth first week such things seemed difficult to find, but we all knew that Jimmy had slept every night, that Vicky's finger-play with her food had diminished and that she had been seen to use a spoon unaided at least twice. We were also pleased with the fact that Edwin had only been dirty three nights out of four and that William had carried the dinner plates to the sink after Thursday lunch. He had dropped them when he got there, but nevertheless he had carried them to the sink when asked, proving that he had some comprehension of his mother tongue. The meeting ended on a high note because we finished on a success, and this in itself was a good pointer to the future. Since then we have always tried to finish every session, no matter how traumatic for us and the child, with a success, so that the last thing the child gets is praise and the staff get the pleasure.

Three weeks after we opened school, we had the official opening. The Lord-Lieutenant kept his promise to perform the opening ceremony. This in itself was a marathon to organise, because invitations had to be sent out to every group that had helped the Society to get this far and there was always a danger that one group or another would be forgotten. This in fact did happen, and I spent a long time afterwards pleading fatigue and confusion to a group of ladies who had raised quite a lot of money. Along with several VIPs and parents, there was a total of two hundred people present on a glorious sunny day in May, and the Lord-Lieutenant cut the tape to the strains of a beautiful fanfare by the trumpeters of the Worcester and Sherwood Foresters, the regiment then stationed at Colchester Garrison. Everyone was extremely moved by it all, especially the parents who had formed the Society and who, at its inception, must have considered this to be a pipe-dream. Now here we were, standing in the garden watching the Vicar from the parish church blessing the school.

As half-term approached, we began to feel that perhaps we were going to get somewhere with the children. The school was taking shape nicely and we felt we were beginning to click as a team. We had to find out each other's idiosyncrasies and test each other's sense of humour. We had to know all our colleagues' strengths and weaknesses and, all in all, the first term together was something of a testing period for us. A constant flow of visitors made life irksome for the girls, but I pointed out to them that as long as they worked there they would have to get used to the idea. Any place that is at all unusual is bound to attract attention from many quarters. We had visiting 'experts' who, I suspect, had come for a sneaky look to improve their sketchy knowledge, so that they could go away pretending to know even more than they did not know in the first place; and we had lots of people coming to give us money, or to see how the money they had already given had been spent.

Eventually I had to limit the numbers of visitors because we found it was having a bad effect on the children. I was also concerned that they were just part of the 'goldfish bowl effect', being stared at as freaks in a side-show. Many visitors were surprised to see five children reasonably well behaved and quiet, and those who had heard me speak at lectures were convinced that I had been exaggerating the situation, even though I pointed out that no child could live in such a state of high tension for twenty-four hours a day. I was also quick to reply that, of course, most of the children had started to respond to our brilliant methods almost as soon as they started to attend the school. Looking back, this was actually true, because they had all been treated to a shock. For the first time in their lives these children had had someone step into their little worlds and try to straighten some of the distortions.

Fortunately for us and for the parents, most of the children had started to respond positively, and we were seeing some signs of slight improvement. Only one child,

William, was failing to respond to all our efforts. He seemed to be totally resistant to everything we tried and he continued to be quite viciously aggressive to all and sundry for a large part of the day. A big headache was that he continually tried to have a go at the other children as well, so we spent a lot of time keeping him away from them. In doing this, of course, we took the brunt of his attacks, and I was genuinely concerned for the well-being of my staff. However, we battled on, fully aware that at the end of each working day we could go home and try to forget the problems of the past few hours. The parents had no such easy way out.

My philosophy that I hold today really evolved during that first term. There is no way that any theories can be applied to all autistic children, because they are all so very different from each other. They must all be treated with the most rigid consistency and, without it, they become even more confused and distraught and even harder to get through to. Getting through is the most vital aspect of the job and, within reason, I am convinced that anything goes if it does get through. When I say 'get through', I am not talking about a child who is made to fear the consequences of not behaving in an acceptable fashion. I am talking about entering a child's world and manipulating him away from the things he does, that we do not consider to be acceptable. The object of the exercise is to leave him with the parts of himself that are acceptable, and to aim towards a child who wants to communicate with the world outside his own and will eventually want other people to share in his world. Perhaps this sounds a little over the top and too unrealistic, but I have always felt that if you aim very high and fall a bit or even a lot short, you still reach a pretty high standard; but if you aim too low in the first place and then fall short, you probably get nowhere at all and frustration, on the part of the adults who are supposed to be normal, results in the sinking of the ship. In this job, once you feel you are achieving nothing, you are dead.

It was because of these views that I formed a theory that applies to all children, and particularly ours: if they can do it, make them; if they cannot do it, teach them. In this way it is hoped that the child can be dragged up by his boot-laces into doing the vital things in life, such as looking after himself. It should go without saying that being able to communicate is a vital part of living, but communication skills, or rather the lack of them, are central to our children's problems, and therefore a separate chapter is devoted to this subject. Having said that, I still feel that it is impossible to start to teach our children to communicate in an acceptable way before we have eliminated behaviour problems associated with the inability to communicate and, in many cases, 'unlearned' many of the behaviour patterns that have been taught into them by so many unwittingly wrong responses to their distorted actions.

I have often wondered what motto I would place over the door of the school if I were asked to do so. Over the door of Strangeways Prison in Manchester it says, 'This place of correction was erected for the benefit of society so that the offender may learn to be rehabilitated and to serve a good and useful life hereafter.' My motto would read on the lines of: 'This school was opened for you, child, so that you can forget the miseries of you own little prison and learn that life can be, if nothing else, a source of pleasure (P.S. if you did it before you came and it was acceptable to everyone, carry on; if it wasn't, leave it outside).'

I have always felt that it is vital to have as much fun as possible with our children; if they can learn to have a giggle, then a tremendous step has been taken. Half-way through the second half of the first term, one visitor commented that she was surprised to see some of the children appearing to be getting some enjoyment from life; this was totally opposed to anything she had ever read in any book. I tried to explain that, above all, I insisted that my children were human beings, and one basic human right should be that a human being is allowed to smile. A benefit from this is that the child learns to relax and, if he can relax, he will not be damaging himself and other people both physically and emotionally. Once he reaches this level of relaxation he can be seen to be open to further teaching. The biggest problem is that it takes so long to get him to this level.

Looking back, I am quite surprised that we were able to produce such thoughts after a relatively short time and I think this is due, in no small measure, to the fact that my staff and I feel we can communicate together well enough for everyone to be able to throw in his or her threepennyworth in all discussions. This means we can pool our ideas and put over our view-points to everyone, and thus everyone can glean his or her own guidelines. In effect, the philosophy I have propounded is not just my own, it is an amalgam of all my colleagues' opinions. The beauty of this is that, when things go wrong, no one can blame me alone because they all thought of it in the first place!

Towards the middle of June that year I was asked to try to organise a trip to London with a small group of children, to help publicise a big fund-raising ball from which we were to get some of the proceeds. A press meeting had been organised by the National Society and the plan was for us to meet some of the Bunny Girls from the Playboy Club. The meeting-place was the statue of Peter Pan in Kensington Gardens, because many people have likened autistic children to Peter Pan since he was very good-looking and seemed to have failed to grow up, as, at first glance, have our children. I fail to see the likeness myself, because Peter Pan never crucified his parents or anyone else around him.

However, we decided that three of our five were now fit to go outside the school, leaving the general population with a fair chance of survival. William was still not fit or safe to take out and J.C.'s parents had warned of a new desire in him to run away. So we decided to take Vicky,

Edwin and Jimmy because these three seemed to have calmed enough to risk it. We had also been told that Edwin seemed to enjoy train rides so much that his mother used to take him on a train to stop his screams, as well as for a treat. Before we left school, it was arranged that he would be taken back immediately if he started to kick up before we got on the train. At least this way he would not be rewarded with something he liked by doing something he should not do. 'What if he kicks up on the train?' came the question. Snookered for a quick response I said, 'I tell you what, that is not very positive thinking, because if trouble is anticipated then you stand a better chance of getting it'—which was a pretty good cover-up on my part because I had not got a clue, either!

We arrived in London without any further problems and the first one we encountered was at Peter Pan's statue. The press had failed to appear, which was hardly surprising as it was absolutely pouring down. The scantily clad Bunny Girls were getting extremely wet, more than the rest of us for obvious reasons. So we all hopped it back to the Bunny Club where a lovely spread was waiting for us. The press men finally arrived and a series of pictures was taken for the evening papers of the children with Babs and Pam, the Bunny Girls. They were both extremely interested in our work and we were well pleased with the way our children had taken to the whole day. We were mostly surprised at the way in which Edwin was controlling himself.

All went well until Edwin's fancy for teeth came to the fore. We were walking past an extremely tall London policeman and Edwin climbed up him. He tried to stick his fingers in the policeman's mouth, shouting, 'See your teeth,' at the top of his lungs. The officer was last seen legging it up Park Lane towards Marble Arch, in total shock, looking for something normal to deal with, like terrorists or bank robbers. To make things less embarrassing the staff member with Edwin was heard to mutter feebly, 'Right! Back to school.' This provided an easy way out, I suppose, yet time and time again parents faced with the public disapproval of their child's behaviour cannot get out of it quite so readily. Comments like 'He needs a good thrashing', 'If I had my way he'd be locked up', 'If I had a child like that I'd have myself sterilised', do not go down too well if you are a parent struggling to control your flesh and blood. If the child is a two-year-old, everyone considers it to be merely a perfectly normal childish paddy, but if that child is fourteen years old or more and extremely strong, then it is a horrific situation to be in. What can be hilarious in a toddler can be pretty hair-raising in a teenager. The whole thing is made so much worse by the fact that these children look so normal and therefore the passing public see no handicap.

The Bunny Girls refused to hear of us going all the way home on the train and insisted on paying for a minicab to take us back to Kelvedon. We were delighted with their generosity and were taken home in a huge Citroën estate. Not only was it a pleasant trip back, but I also felt that I had the chance to educate yet another member of the public, the driver, who was certainly astonished to realise that such children existed. The only problem we experienced on the way back was from Edwin. When we were within quarter of a mile of the school, he suddenly went mad, and it took three adults to contain this raging six-year-old. We could only guess that his reason was, to him at least, a good one. Perhaps he could not handle the thought of going back to school because he knew that the school was the place that tried to make him conform. I suppose we shall never know.

As the term drew to a close we continued to experience a range of problems, but we had quite a few laughs and giggles. Four of the five children were surviving the course and the staff seemed in good order, but, sad to say, William was achieving absolutely nothing in the way of learning to control his temper, although he had learnt a few things, like the need to sit and wait for his food. The only really positive thing that we got over to him was the fact that he could only have seconds of any course, as opposed to being allowed to keep eating until every pan was empty. It took us several weeks of trying, but he had to be made to realise that we meant business. Whatever the retaliation he chose as a result of our saying 'no', nothing would induce us to give in. It was a hard lesson for him to learn, but learn it he did, at the expense of our nerves and sanity.

Whatever happened in that term, we always had the consolation of knowing that at least we had a school and, against all the odds, we had fulfilled the dreams of the parents. Even for the parents of the most difficult children, we were at least providing a much-needed break for four nights and five days a week. Finally, I told my staff, as we drank a bottle or three of wine to celebrate the end of term, there was always next term to continue getting through to those very frightened and sometimes frightening children.

5

DEALING WITH BEHAVIOUR PROBLEMS

If only we had known what the start of the second term was to be like, we would never have described Opening Day as disastrous. Compared with what we let ourselves in for in September, Opening Day had been a cakewalk.

Firstly, we had the original five children to contend with. They were fresh from six weeks' holiday at home and had totally regressed, I suppose because the previous term had not been long enough for us to imprint our viewpoint indelibly on them. In this respect, 4th September, 1977, was a carbon copy of the first time they had set foot in the place. On top of this, we had half a dozen new children to contend with. That day still features prominently among my nightmares. Every single child seemed hell-bent on flexing his distorted ego and on generally throwing his weight around. New staff had been taken on to cater for the fresh influx, but they were as raw as the original crew had been; they had to be trained from scratch.

The first new child in was an eleven-year-old boy called Stewart. He had spent the greater part of his life screaming and yelling and had driven his parents to despair. His mother's first request was for us to stop his head-banging. 'I don't care how you stop it, just please stop it,' she stated quite categorically. It seemed that everything you said to him was enough to trigger him off. He was, and had been for several years, on three doses per day of each of the following drugs: Stelazine, Sparine and Tryptizol, each of which is a major tranquilliser and any one of which should flatten the average adult for a long time. We could only assume that, before he started on them, he must have been absolutely out of control, because even with these dreadful drugs he was exceptionally difficult. Unless, of course, the wretched stuff was making him worse.

The first thing I asked the parents was for their permission to wean him off the medication, explaining that I could not hope even to begin to see their child in his true light until he was functioning without the influence of the tranquillisers. His mother reported that he had been on them for years and that she had just obtained one repeat prescription after another. Not one doctor had been there to monitor the effects. If the drugs had had a beneficial effect, I could have just about seen the sense of their being prescribed, but they did not appear to have helped him in the slightest. I contacted our School Medical Officer who came into school to see Stewart. She expressed horror at the dosages and gave us a time schedule to help reduce and then eliminate them. It was set out over several weeks, because medication cannot suddenly be cut out.

As the days progressed we saw no improvement, which was exactly as we had expected; but more importantly, we saw no deterioration at all. He continued to bash his head and to yell and howl the place down for most of his waking day. We tried several behaviour modification techniques, all to no avail. We started with time-out in the isolation room—a total waste of time. Written records at the end of the two-week trial showed no reduction in frequency of self-injurious behaviour at all, nor did they show any particular pattern. We tried positive reinforcement, whereby he was given acres of niceness every time he was quiet. No success. We linked the two together to see if the exaggerated difference between the two treatments he was getting would have any impact. We still got nowhere. We tried good old-fashioned playing merry hell with him to see if we could shock him out of it. That failed. We tried slapping him on his hand to see if a physical shock would work—it did not.

I then tried something which, in retrospect, was rather silly. The next time he banged his head I copied him, to see if he might be made to realise that he was not the only one able to perform in his usual way. He was literally drumming his head on a door frame, so I took a deep breath and launched myself at the door. No fool, me—I reckoned that at least the door would fly open, giving me a chance of survival. The impact on Stewart was astounding: he did not even bat an eyelid, but I do think that, as I sank to a chair to recover, he glanced at me with a look of 'useless amateur' on his face.

We thought of other approaches to try. He had precious little comprehension, which made it extremely difficult to get through to him, as everything we could do for him and with him had to be done on a demonstration level. I was convinced that unless we stopped the head-banging tempers we would never get through to him on any other level. There seemed to be nothing he enjoyed doing which could be used as a positive replacement for his usual tricks, so eventually I took a decision which I knew I might regret for a long time, but for the child's sake and that of his parents it had to be worth a try. It was not something which I chose to do lightly; it was not, under any circumstances, to be tried by any other member of staff. Like most approaches to these children it was to be totally geared to this one particular child and certainly not to the others. I stressed all this very forcibly to my staff individually, because there was no way that I wanted anyone to be under the illusion that I was advocating this method for any child who was a head-banger.

I reasoned that many or even most of Stewart's outbursts were designed by him to be a manipulation exercise, and that this had been reinforced by the response he had received over many years. Every time he had been asked to do something he had blown his top, so everyone around him had backed off to keep the peace.

The very next time he banged his head I grabbed hold of him, dropped him to the floor and banged his head for him six times. I felt that a few more bangs on top of all those he had inflicted on himself would not do much more harm, and I certainly did not bang it as hard as he normally did himself. I wanted him to see that he, too, could be manipulated. I stopped and roared at him to do it again. For the first time in his life he spoke a word of English with meaning. He said, 'No,' and he never banged his head again. This method has never been used since, but I must add that if an identical situation arose with another child, I would not hesitate to consider trying it again if all else failed.

After this Stewart was a changed boy. He began to enjoy life and we were able to fill his days with much more useful activities. He absolutely loved swimming, and he began to paint with gusto—nothing over-creative, but a great source of fun for him. His people were extremely weird, all with spiky hair and very large navels and enormous popping eyes. His first effort was proudly displayed on the wall in the entrance hall, having been framed at great expense, only to be snaffled by his mother when she came to a parents' evening. It still hangs on her lounge wall to be shown off every time they have a visitor. Stewart also learned to ride a bike and spent many happy hours circling the playground. The only problem was that he insisted on going round in the same direction all the time and we had to force him to go the other way now and again to get the tyres to wear evenly!

He also learned a good number of domestic skills. He loved to make his own bed and to clean his bedroom. He became a dab hand at washing up and drying the dishes but he was at his happiest peeling potatoes. He grasped the idea very readily and was left to his own devices. The cook kept a close watch on him and, as his teacher returned to the kitchen, she heard the cook saying, 'No, Stewart, big potatoes, please.' Stewart was creasing himself laughing and the potatoes had been reduced to the size of peas. It was almost as if he was trying to find something in the centre. After that the catchword became 'Big potatoes, please, Stewart!'.

One day he was given some cheese to grate, and this incident highlights the way in which these children need to have every little step taught in. Nobody had bothered to tell him that you stop when you get to the end of the piece of cheese and so he continued, grating the tips of the fingers on his right hand. He stared at the blood and said, in a very plaintive voice, 'Ouch!' A short time before, when he was at his worst, it would have been impossible to imagine him being prepared to do something as valuable as grating cheese, but he would certainly have done a lot more than just say 'Ouch'. A very unorthodox child had been treated in a very unorthodox way and we had got through to him.

As Stewart continued his raging bull antics at the start of that term, the original five children were still up to their old tricks. J.C. was still into doorknobs. Vicky was back to her glug-glugging and had developed a new pastime: slapping herself in the face quite viciously; Edwin was back to demanding his own way all the time, teaching the new ones what it was all about. The new children did not really need any teaching; they all seemed to be past masters in the art of disruption.

James and Mark were like twins. They had both spent long periods in the same subnormality hospital and had many of the stereotyped behaviour patterns which seem to grow in such places. They were very institutionalised in their ways. I am not knocking the efforts of the staff in hospitals, but the lack of numbers and facilities, at least in the past, prevented staff from being much more than minders. These two twelve-year-olds had had very little time spent on them in the self-care line and both were on medication when they came to us. They were given to very severe aggression to staff and were particularly adept at biting. Neither of them was anywhere near being toilet-trained and both were projectile vomiters. The drugs that these boys were on appeared, as in Stewart's case, to be achieving absolutely zero. If the medication was supposed to be calming them down, then they must have been pretty horrendous without it. Their behaviour was totally uncontrollable; even some of the other children were terrified of them and several members of staff expressed their serious concern for their own safety. I knew my staff well enough, even in this short time, to realise that they were not exaggerating.

I called a case conference with the social workers involved and with my governors, and put it to them that we could not tolerate or begin to cope with such incredible disturbance; the school was simply not geared to this sort of behaviour. A medical decision was taken to alter the medication and, in James's case, it seemed initially to have a beneficial effect. An added bonus for him was that his parents found themselves able to have him at home and they seemed to cope.

Unfortunately, in Mark's case, he could not go home as he had no parents. He had been adopted but, sad to say, his adoptive parents, on finding out, when he was two, that he was handicapped, had abandoned him and ever since then, his Social Worker told me, he had been hospitalised. This meant that Mark had been in a subnormality hospital for ten years. Every Friday, when the other children went home, he went back from living in our group setting to another group setting and, because of the huge staff turnover at the hospital, the poor kid hardly knew which staff he would see the following weekend. He proved to be completely incapable of taking the fantastic change of routine and it was with great reluctance that I had to recommend his removal from school. The same thing was to happen a few months later with James and William. They both continued to be aggressive and eventually finished up attacking the other children. I am saddened but not ashamed to admit that our school totally failed to help these three children in any way.

The staff were struggling under the onslaught of all the

problems that we were facing, but I kept telling them that we were lucky. These children's parents had put up with this sort of behaviour for years. Having said that, however, I was not suggesting that we should put up with it, too. So a long discussion about an out-and-out attack was started. We all decided that, as meal-times form an integral part of the family structure, and we counted ourselves as a family, too, then we would use meal-times as a base-line to work from. We all hoped that what we were about to do would spread over into other parts of the day as well.

The next lunch-time, we all marched into the dining-room, took a child each and made it very clear that any action apart from eating was taboo. It took three weeks of the most difficult labours ever, and chaos was the order of the day. However, as I pointed out to one of the girls when she said how dreadful it had been, it had also been pretty dreadful before we took this new tack, but at least now we felt that we were trying something positive. If an outsider had walked in during any of these meal-times he would have thought that he was in bedlam. We witnessed plates and cutlery, chairs and tables go flying across the room. We had children screaming, yelling and making themselves sick. We had staff almost reduced to tears. Eventually, however, many of the children began to realise that in the normal course of events you sit down to eat, that you make some effort to ensure that your plate stays on the table rather than lying shattered on the floor and that food only goes in your mouth.

Some people have commented to me that they feel such methods are too negative, and one person even suggested that we were being cruel. Two points come to mind in answer to such suggestions. Firstly, I shall insist until the day I retire that the cruelty lies in not intervening in the grossly distorted lives of our children, and we have all too often seen the results of this non-intervention. Secondly, to those who talk of negativism and cruelty, I would say that they must have been very negative in their own thoughts to have missed the praise which was and still is lavished on any child at Doucecroft who does something right; if they had only looked more carefully they would have noticed praise being poured forth every time a child swallowed the tiniest mouthful of food.

As I have made several references to behaviour modification, perhaps this is as good a place as any to expound a little on my views of this extremely useful tool in relation to the children I work with. One dictionary definition of behaviour is 'the way in which an organism functions within its environment', and to modify means to 'alter or change', with the inference that the alteration or change is for the better. Many volumes of closely detailed studies have been published on the subject and they are all extremely complex. I have preferred to take the basic theories and alter them to suit my children's needs. All teachers spend their entire day modifying the behaviour of their pupils, whether or not they are handicapped. Here is an extremely simple example. A child is talking in class. The teacher tells him to be quiet. The child stops. His behaviour has been modified. However, the teacher now has two ways to go. If he praises the child by saying 'Thank you, that's better', there is far more chance that the child will have his behaviour modified permanently because he appreciates the praise and the recognition that he has done something right, i.e., that which he was asked to do. If, on the other hand, the teacher says, 'That's better, you horrible little brat,' or words to that effect, there is more chance of a repetition of the 'offence' because the child has received no recognition of his correct actions.

In the above example there are technical terms which could be applied. The child praised for being quiet receives a 'positive reinforcer'. The one faced with sarcasm and insult receives a 'negative reinforcer'; because all children need attention, he might continue to misbehave to get more attention and eventually lose sight of the fact that only positive attention is worth having. Perhaps it can be seen from these examples that behaviour modification is only useful if it is used with great wariness. I cannot accept that it is a universal panacea, but used sensibly, with intensive communication between the carers running the programmes, it can certainly be very beneficial in helping to eliminate undesirable patterns. It is vital to understand exactly what you are offering the child, because it is so easy to reinforce wrong things. A child does not suddenly 'pick up' wrong behaviour; it is taught in to him, in the same way that correct behaviour is taught in.

How often do you see a mother outside a shop giving her child a bar of chocolate to stop him screaming in his buggy, without realising for one moment that she is saying, 'Well done for screaming, here is your reward.' The beginning of any behavioural pattern is determined by the response given the first time the behaviour appears. The child quickly learns that a lovely soft cuddle in the midst of a full-blown temper tantrum can be extremely pleasant and is therefore a signal to prolong the tantrum.

When a child starts at Doucecroft, we invariably find that many unacceptable facets have become so firmly entrenched over a long period that the family can no longer cope and the child has to be sent away to school. Then we find ourselves trying to get involved in what can be a very protracted unlearning process. Bearing in mind that in this book I am not talking about all autistic children, but only about those I have experienced at Doucecroft, very few of these children have been quiet and withdrawn on arrival. The majority have been very easily disturbed and unable to tolerate much frustration, so our first task is normally to try to get the child calm enough for us to be able to teach him some of the finer points of life. The first time you try to impose your will on a child who, to all intents and purposes, is hell-bent on destroying himself and his surroundings, the effect can be dramatic. The screams may rise to a crescendo and any self-inflicted injuries may get worse and worse until the child realises that the people trying, for the first time in his life, to bar him, rigidly and consistently, from indulging in his distorted approach to life, are actually determined to win. As you have read above, in some cases we fail, but in most cases we seem to win and then the child can begin to settle down and start to appreciate the constraints on him; with that, a stable, secure environment can follow.

We have tried many tacks with our children's problems and I am totally committed to the theory that any treatment within reason is acceptable. I feel that any strategy that succeeds in stopping a negative action is in itself positive, but only if the most important word in my philosophy is applied at the same time. That word is 'positivism'. That is to say, it is totally useless to sanction a child for doing something wrong and then to fail in the most vital area of all: that of reinforcing his compliance with your demand by praising him immediately. It is never enough to praise a child just for doing something right. He simply must, repeat *must*, be praised for ceasing to do something wrong. I would strongly advocate this approach for all children, not only mine. The child ultimately gets praised twice as much, which has to be a good thing. I can only repeat that negativism lies in non-intervention, thus allowing unacceptable patterns to continue. Every effort should and must be made to render the child acceptable and manageable. I feel strongly that unless these efforts are going to be made, we have no right whatsoever to take the child out of his current environment and drop him into an identical one, because in doing this nothing has changed for him.

Sanctions for our children, like rewards, have to be instantaneous: such as removing a child's meal for eating badly. If one of my children has to be made aware of his shortcomings he must know immediately, just as he must have his good points praised instantly. A far cry indeed from mainstream schools, where an offence on Monday leads to detention on Friday, an offence on Friday leads to the boss's office on Monday, and swearing at the teacher on Tuesday leads to a missed swimming lesson on Thursday.

One of the most controversial forms of behaviour modification is the use of what is euphemistically called 'physical sanction'. Personally, preferring to call a spade a spade, I refer to such a sanction as a smack. This most emotive of subjects has even spurred one group of teachers to form an organisation to ban any form of physical sanction. Some countries have already banned it and England is well on the way to doing so. As soon as the word 'smack' gets a mention some people fly up in the air and raise their hands in horror. Few subjects apart from abortion, religion and politics cause more heated debate. What I want to say is that if such treatment of a child is ever to be considered of any value, its use must be very, very carefully controlled. I have never been an advocate of giving any child a slap as a first resort; it has always been suggested well down the list when many other tactics have failed; but neither do I advocate it as the last resort.

Whenever 'physical sanction' is used at Doucecroft, it is always done following the same rigid guidelines. No child is ever smacked without prior agreement from me, and this follows discussion of the subject in relation to the particular child under review, and to the particular offence for which the correct sanction is being sought. Thus it may be that a child is doing ten things wrong, but would only be given a slap for one particular thing. The decision to do so would only be taken if the general consensus was that the slap would have some useful effect on the child, i.e. it would stop the child's negative action. Thus the child is not slapped for having done something wrong, rather he is slapped while actually doing it.

An example may best serve to explain. J.C. used to bang the door constantly, either in a rage or just for the

sheer hell of it. We tried everything we could thi
stop him, from telling him off very sternly to forc
to sit in a corner, which he hated. All attempts fai
I instructed staff to slap him firmly on his leg every
time he slammed a door on purpose. It was only needed a few times before the shock brought him to his senses. It seemed that the other approaches had been too complex for him to grasp, or that they had been too prolonged, but a short sharp shock had the desired effect.

If administered willy-nilly, I can see that physical sanction can get out of control and that it can indeed come to be used as a first resort and then as the only resort; but if everything is set out very clearly first and the monitoring is precise, and especially if the stopping of the action is followed, as ever, by praise, I fail to see how smacking a child at specific junctures can be construed as anything but the right course of action. A common enough expression used by people involved with children is, 'That child needs a good smack for doing that.' The danger lies in then administering the smack without considering beforehand if it is really felt that that is what would help the child to overcome his problem. As I said earlier, a very emotive subject indeed.

Soon after the half-way point in that second term, we began to feel that our efforts were beginning to pay off, at least with some of the children. A few were really beginning to enjoy life as we so-called normal people felt they should. We were able to take them on long walks and came back commenting on how pleasant things had been. Meal-times were starting to become much less of a trial and one or two staff were commenting that they had actually enjoyed their food. A good sign of the confidence of the staff was shown when we were offered the chance to take some children on holiday to Sussex. The plan was to take nine children and seven staff. There was a scramble by the staff to get places, which made me feel very pleased. We received encouragement from some of the parents, who wrote in with comments like, 'We went in a café on Saturday and we weren't asked to leave.' These comments were our best indication that we were on the right lines, although several of the children continued to try to put us through the mill.

The night staff took the brunt of the continued onslaught. There were only two of them and they used to wonder if these non-communicating children were laughing up their sleeves in the bedrooms, drawing lots for a turn to be horrible that night and deciding who was going to do what and to whom. The vision of a group of our children having such a get-together has often flashed through my mind. The biggest problem for the night staff in those early days was that none of the children slept very heavily, and regular visits to the bedroom were likely to disturb some of them even more. So the staff had the unenviable task of choosing between the possibility of a child being up and creating havoc, or the almost absolute certainty of a bedroomful being woken as they entered and perhaps joining in the havoc, which might not even have happened, but for their interference.

Vicky had suddenly devised a new trick, as I mentioned earlier. For no apparent reason she began to slap her face, quite gently at first but with increasing frequency. Before we even realised that it was the start of a big problem, she was literally hammering herself in the face with both hands. She was doing it at night in bed and even in her sleep. An extra staff meeting was called and we discussed all the possibilities. It was straight away decided that we would definitely not smack her when she smacked herself. This decision was taken because everyone felt that they knew her well enough, even after such a short time, to realise that she would not respond to this idea. There were no specific reasons why; it was more a feeling, which arises occasionally when choices have to be made. I suppose it could be a form of intuition, on which perhaps good teaching should be based and then tempered with the tools of the trade, like the behaviour modification techniques I have described.

Having chosen what not to do in Vicky's case, we then decided to have a monitoring period. This was needed to give us the chance to establish a base-line to work from. This is a vital step in all problem-solving, because it gives an accurate picture of any decrease in frequency of any activity once a chosen programme is put into operation. The opposite can also occur, where an increase is noticed at first until the child cottons on to what is happening to him, and could also signify that the chosen programme is the wrong one. Either way it is necessary to have a very accurate picture of the scene. Without it, it is possible to distort the true picture quite significantly.

In Vicky's case, we took a count of face slaps for five days and saw a pattern of up to five hundred slaps a day. Each one was vicious and she very rapidly began to have severe bruises on both cheeks. One of the staff recalled that, for something she could not remember that Vicky had done, she had held tightly to the child's hands while she had shouted at her not to do it again. Vicky had been very upset but the incident had not recurred. This was felt to be the answer, so it was decided that the next time Vicky slapped herself she would be laid face down on the floor, the staff member dealing with her would straddle her, hold her arms firmly behind her back and roar loudly, 'No, don't slap your face.'

The first time it was done, any passer-by would have thought that someone was being murdered! She screamed and glugged, she yelled and howled, but it was fifteen minutes before she slapped herself again, when the treatment was repeated. The same reaction was forthcoming and the delay was even longer. At the end of the first day she had been 'floored' some fifty-seven times, and this dramatic decrease was enough to tell us it was the right way to face the problem. The next day the treatment only needed doing thirty-odd times and the next only fifteen or so. The fourth day we were down to four and on the Friday it was not used at all. I was able to ring Vicky's mother and give her the good news, and to tell her what to do if the same thing began over the weekend. It did not, but on the Monday morning, as Vicky came back into school, her teacher opened the door to the taxi. Vicky walked straight up to her and tapped herself very lightly on each cheek. Her teacher had a feeling that Vicky was seeking to confirm that she would get the same treatment if she did it again. She got it immediately and she was never seen to slap herself again.

It was not really possible to give her praise for not slapping her face, because after the treatment, it would have made no sense at all to her to say 'good girl', and indeed could have confused her further. She might have thought she was being praised for screaming, which was the last thing she had done. Instead, we made a great point of giving her a lot of attention when she was being nice to us. We are convinced that if her teacher had not floored her that last time she would have started again very soon and would quickly have been back to five hundred times a day.

We found in the main that the children were positively responding to us and that many of them were showing signs of being able to tolerate frustration more easily. We saw instances of children seeming to realise that we were there to try to help them, to try to give them some pattern, security and stability in their hitherto fragmented and unhappy lives. We also saw signs that some of the children were trying to exercise some form of self-control and, albeit very slowly, we were approaching a state of calm, in which we might be able to have a real go at teaching some of the children to communicate in whichever way we could manage.

6

COMMUNICATION SKILLS

It is a very sweeping statement to say that we planned to teach our children to communicate. Communication involves an extremely wide range of processes and skills which, all too often, we take for granted. Analysis of these processes and skills will perhaps serve to show the miracle that occurs each time a child develops his communication skills and may also make it less surprising that some children, like ours, fail to develop their skills.

When a child enters the world he is effectively unable to communicate, yet in a very short time he learns about words, to say them first without comprehension and then with; he learns to string words together into meaningless gibberish and then into meaningful sentences. He picks up expressions and uses them freely. He learns to express concrete ideas followed by concepts. He then realises that words change their value with changes in tone of voice, so that 'good boy' can change its meaning to 'not good boy' if sarcasm has been used. He learns the difference between 'I' and 'me' or 'you' and manages to control his environment through using his language. As well as learning the spoken word, the child also starts to understand non-verbal language, such as facial expression, gesture, mime and body language. Remote systems of communication also enter his brain and he learns to use them quite easily. He learns that a ringing telephone is someone trying to communicate and that a ringing door bell or a knock at the door indicates someone's presence at the door. Flashing headlights and car horns become meaningful, as do a myriad other sounds which he learns to filter out of the general hubbub of noise around him.

All these skills come slowly but readily to a child, with apparently little effort. The pattern of development probably goes like this. Little Johnny goes into the kitchen at the age of fourteen months. He has long since established the earliest form of communication by giving and taking eye contact and he has the basics of social communication, because of the relationship with his mother. He reaches Mum in the kitchen and tells her he wants a drink. Because his brain is not yet mature enough for him to talk, the request for a drink comes out as 'Grunt'. Mum pats him on the head and says, 'Hello, darling', which he finds disconcerting. So he repeats the grunt and Mum responds in the same fashion. By this time his thirst is getting stronger and he begins to really pester Mum. She has had enough of him by now and decides that he is being a nuisance, so she tells him to be quiet. His thirst has now reached epic proportions and he begins to get very wound up. Mum banishes him from the kitchen and dumps him on the floor in the lounge, returning to the kitchen where she slams the door behind her.

Johnny has totally failed to get through to her and decides to show his frustration and teach her a lesson. He starts to throw his weight around, without once stopping to think that the failure in communication came from him. He screams and howls, then stops to listen. She's not coming. 'Right, that's it, mother, now cop for this,' and, without further ado, he launches into a full-blown state of demented screaming, commonly known in this trade as a TT, or temper tantrum. Suddenly, however, he goes over the top and bashes his head on the floor, but that shocks and hurts him because his brain, although too immature to let him speak, is certainly mature enough to let him feel pain. The head-banging stops or becomes more gentle, or he is even canny enough to find something softer to bang his head on. To impress Mum further he increases the noise level, so that she will think his death is imminent and, hopefully, will come to the rescue. During this time he may have bitten his fist in pure rage, but again not too hard after the first time.

Eventually Mum does come to the rescue and she works out that he may be thirsty. She gives him a drink and his frustration has been relieved. At the same time she does something which is vital. As the drink is proffered she uses a sound, which in English is 'drink'. He does not use the word yet, but it sinks into the depths of his memory bank.

A few months later the same scene is set. Johnny toddles into the kitchen and asks Mum for a drink. This time his brain has done wonders. He produces a sound which, he has learnt, in the past produced a drink every time his Mum said it. His brain has delved into its depths and come up with the sound he has heard so many times. He says 'drink' but it comes out as 'dink' because he cannot yet get his tongue around the 'dr' sound. However, the sound has the desired effect: he gets his drink and yet again Mum repeats the correct word. His brain takes over and stores it again and, after a few false starts, he is eventually able to say 'drink'. As the months pass, little Johnny learns that instead of saying 'drink' he can string a few words together which indicate his need. He has frequently heard his mother say, 'Do you want a drink?' or, 'There's your drink', and he uses the two to express his need. Eventually, his brain tells him that it is about time he started speaking correctly, so he tries his hand at saying, 'I want a drink'. Unfortunately, he has never heard himself referred to as 'I' because everyone else calls him 'you'. He has heard other people call themselves 'me', so, while he is in the process of confusing everything, he says, 'Me want a drink'. The adult corrects him and again his brain absorbs the message. My daughter once said, 'Me are poorly.' I said, 'I am poorly.' She said, 'Me are as well, let's lie down.'

As Johnny gets older, he sorts out the differences in an amazingly complex communication system and then has to learn 'please' and 'thank you', the two most difficult words for any parent to teach in any language! By the age of five or six, he has some thousands of words in his brain. He does not use them all and the size of his vocabulary is determined by that used in his environment. All shades of meanings of words start to become apparent to him; he has become sensitive to other people's moods and vibrations and, at this stage, is well on his way to becoming a well-rounded, perfectly acceptable human being. At the same time he has developed his social communication skills and has formed many relationships with those people around him.

On the other hand, if something in little Johnny's brain has gone wrong, possibly a chemical reaction taking place or failing to do so, then this unbelievably intricate series of learning processes fails to occur, or occurs in an extremely fragmented fashion. In the brain of the autistic child, it seems that this is exactly what has happened and he is bereft of the brain power to slot all the skills for communication into place. The cause is unknown but the result is clear. The child is left without the basic tools of the trade for living and so he is terrified of the world around him and especially of people, who are able to demand so much of him without his having a chance of coping. Although all autistic children are affected on a sort of sliding scale of handicap, with some who can cope a little and others who appear to having no resources at all, they are all struggling and only a few can actually manage. Instead the child tends to create his own world by lapsing into obsessional, inflexible activities which are described as 'stereotyped behaviour' and tends to cling tenaciously to the same routine, as a way of keeping some stability in his life.

As I have already said, many non-handicapped children go through this sort of stage in which they have their own patterns which seem deeply entrenched. Many, many children play games like avoiding cracks on a pavement, or insist on trying to touch all the rails on a fence as they pass. This is the way most children make themselves feel secure in a very changing world; then, as they develop their communication skills, they also learn to manipulate their environment with those skills. The autistic child fails to develop his skills and so he clings to his routine. Without it he feels he would go mad.

The major part of our work, once we have calmed the child down, is to act as communication therapists, and the whole school is geared to this end. We try to bring language into everything we do, but we do not concentrate solely on the use of the spoken word because there is always more than one way to skin the cat. There is often criticism of alternatives to spoken language, that they are used as a replacement for the spoken word and are 'limited'. Unfortunately, if there is insistence on teaching a child to verbalise only, there is the possibility that he will enter the stage of parroting, simply repeating everything he hears, assuming he starts at all. This can lead to a mind-blowing situation for the family who, having wanted their child to speak following possible years of muteness, may find themselves driven to distraction by endless chuntering of meaningless nonsense.

I feel that it is much more important to try to get the child to signify his needs in a meaningful way by any method that suits him. If his brain is preventing him from speaking it is possible that he can still learn to express himself through gestures or sign language. We do it all the time without even considering what we are doing. For example, if I am on the 'phone and my secretary wants to know if I would like a cup of coffee, she does not need to interrupt my conversation. She asks me a question with a hand sign to show 'drink' and a facial expression, raised eyebrows, to indicate the question. If I would like a cup, I nod or give a thumbs up sign, and if the answer is 'no' I simply shake my head. All the time that this conversation has been going on, I have continued the verbal one with the person on the other end of the line.

At Doucecroft we have made extensive use of a signing system called Makaton, a very simple series of hand signs designed by a team of speech therapists. Many of the gestures are the international signs used to show common things. The drink sign, for example, is the cupped hand raised to the mouth. The idea with Makaton is to employ it as a communication system and as a possible aid to future language. It is always used in conjunction with the spoken word, because the hope is that the child will one day speak, and speak with meaning. Sign language at all times must be considered as a replacement of muteness, never as a replacement for language. If the child fails to develop spoken language, he still finishes up with the ability to tell people of his needs.

If used sensibly and correctly, sign systems like Makaton can be a boon, if used wrongly, a disaster. In another school I heard a child, verbally mute for years, say 'toilet' to his teacher, who had for years painstakingly taught him to use Makaton and now, for the first time he had vocalised instead. He was a cerebral palsied child and saying the word was a real struggle. The teacher told him he could go to the toilet but first he must sign for it. By the time he had signed, he had wet himself. I always thought that it was the children who were supposed to have the problems!

When we use Makaton signs with our children, we discuss each child in turn to decide which words he needs. Most often these are words like 'toilet' and 'biscuit' to start with, because toileting is a crucial factor on the way to acceptability and biscuits are usually popular enough for the child to be persuaded to ask for them. The staff member working with the child on the sign for toilet uses the sign in the toilet, and says the word at the same time. The child's hand is manipulated to make the sign which is a stroke of the middle finger of one hand on the opposite side of the chest. We accept anything vaguely like the correct sign, so long as the child has indicated his need. Some people have been known to try to get the child to sign exactly as shown in the manual, but I think that this is as bad as demanding that a child speaking for the first time should pronounce the word with total accuracy, and I do not think that it is necessary. If the sign is made in an understandable way without complete accuracy it is much akin to a speaking child using slang, but it is better than having the child wet himself.

When this process of teaching is going on, it is easy to expect results too quickly or to see the child sign once or twice and then assume he can do so reliably at all times. This is an easy mistake to make. We overcome it by keeping a chart record. The chart is kept as simple as possible because complex recording is a waste of time and can distract the teacher from the child; some of our children are quick enough to destroy the toilet in that short time. Our records simply state the following: the number of demonstrations, the number of refusals and the number of successes. Once we have ten consecutive successes we consider the sign to be known. The child is then consistently asked to sign each time, to reinforce his new-found knowledge. If he is bursting to go to the toilet, he is shown the sign and asked to make it after he has relieved himself, which prevents an accident.

It can take months and months of patient effort to teach the sign and, even after such efforts, some of our children have still failed to grasp the point of the exercise. Quite a few children, however, have picked up signs fairly readily and, once they have learnt one sign, they seem almost relieved to have found a way of getting through to us and go on to several more. As the child's ability to use and understand signs grows we slot in more and more. The words we choose are always relevant to the child's lifestyle and we always make a point of teaching the signs to the parents as well, because failure to do that would be dropping the child and the family further into hot water then they were before.

I knew a child in Yorkshire who was taught a signing system at her school. It was known as Paget-Gorman and was an extremely complex system which had its own grammatical structure, as opposed to Makaton which is more or less a vocabulary list. The child was picked to be taught Paget-Gorman for the same reasons that we picked the children for Makaton, because it was felt after discussion that they were able to catch on and benefit. This girl proved her school staff right. She picked up the system extremely quickly and the teacher, a very skilled instructor, was delighted. The girl not only signed fluently, she most definitely understood as well and was like a child released from prison. Only one mistake was made. It was a termly boarding school and the programme began at the start of a term. Come the term's end, she went home. *Nobody* had told her parents and they had no opportunity to learn the system. The child was most put out. For nine years her parents had agonised over her inability to communicate and now, here she was, trying desperately to get herself over to them and they did not understand a thing. Not surprisingly, she was super-aggrieved and her parents had to ring the school. The teacher of Paget-Gorman felt so sorry for the child and her family that she went to their home for the week and saved them all from total disaster.

'If it gets through and they can get back to us, it does not matter which way we go.' I reckon that is as good a starting point as any on the long road to communication. Perhaps it was for this reason that I once popped into the local DIY shop and borrowed a set of Formica samples. They were some 8 × 5 cms and perfect for an idea which had suddenly come to mind. I had long thought of a way for a child to have something useful and handy to show his needs quickly and simply if he could not sign. The Formica pieces were just right. I took them to a local plastics factory and they cut me a few dozen pieces of perspex of the same size. Pictures cut from catalogues were sandwiched between the perspex and Formica, along with strips of double-sided sticky tape. (Sellotape Scotch Pads would have served the same purpose.) We then had more or less indestructible talking pictures through the edge of which I drilled a hole. A few metal rings suitable for keys were cadged from the same DIY shop, who fortunately forgot about their Formica bits, and the children had their pictures to hand on a belt round their waists. This cut down their frustration and helped enormously.

As well as introducing Makaton and the talking pictures, we also started sessions which we call SI or Social Interaction. We split the children into ability groups and twice a week they go into different rooms for a session of some sort of interaction activity involving communication techniques. The most able children, that is the verbal ones, have to tell each other what they had for lunch, where they went for their walk that morning, and so on; the middle group, who can use Makaton but cannot speak, have a sign practising lesson and learn some new signs, usually those which we feel have some interest for them. For example, Scott, a child who came to us in 1983, loves all forms of transport, so he has learnt the signs for car, bus, boat, plane, bike and train. Not a lot of use to a child, you might say, but his parents report that he loves to go through a scrap-book of pictures that we asked them to make, and he names each item by signing. The beauty of this activity is that he sits on their laps and cuddles up to them during these sessions at home, and he loves it just as much as they do; at one time they could not get near him.

The less able children have a session where they learn the names of the others in the group, body parts and the names of items in the room. In this way it is hoped that they will become more aware of other people and of their environment. Occasionally some of the children are withdrawn from their groups for individual sessions on intensive programmes. Jane was one such child. In many months we had failed to achieve any eye contact with her at all. It is quite common for autistic children to give no eye contact which, in the average child, is present at about six weeks of age but is often a pointer to parents at an early stage in the autistic child's life that there is in fact a problem.

In Jane's case we were achieving precious little in the co-operation stakes, so we decided to introduce a programme to 'train in' more eye contact. We knew she loved to eat raisins, so we started to train this little six year-old with a system of positively reinforcing raisins. The pattern went like this. The girl working with her sat opposite and held her hand. Then she called, 'Jane'. If Jane looked at her, this was a score and a circle was drawn on a chart which was marked out in sessions. If she failed to look, a cross was entered and if she looked for more than a count of two she scored a filled-in circle. The very second a score was made, she received a raisin. Her name was called for a period of five minutes and there were eight such periods, spaced out as evenly as possible over the day. The record chart, as usual, was very useful. Without a record in detail it would have been easy to convince ourselves that there was or was not an improvement, and it is simple enough to imagine things happening. You are hoping for an improvement and it could follow that you might imagine the improvement you wanted, rather than a decline. With a filled-in chart the change would be undeniable. In Jane's case, after three months, when the results were plotted on a graph, the line rocketed ever upwards and, a month after that, we could state quite positively that Jane responded to her name one hundred per cent. The big spin-off was that Jane began to co-operate a little more at the table and in the bath, and she certainly became more aware of the people around her.

As ever, one-off approaches to getting language from a child have shown to be the most effective. Jimmy had never spoken, but we found out on his first day that he loved being tickled, so we tickled him whenever he came near us. He revelled in the attention, but as soon as we got him coming back for more, we put a condition on it.

We spent hours in a concerted effort to get him to say 'tickle'. It was a rule that he was to get no tickle unless he tried to say the word first. If he started to say it, the tickle came before he had finished speaking. Three weeks later, he got his first tickle under the new regime because he muttered a sound which was as similar to 'tickle' as made no difference. Three weeks further on we had built into him 'want a tickle'. After that it was reasonably straightforward to substitute other words, such as 'drink', and then we got 'please' at the end and soon he was asking for things quite readily, in a completely acceptable way. Coupled with the Makaton he learned, he can express most of his needs. He now signs and speaks and eventually we shall encourage him to drop the signs.

An aspect of communication that I stress is physical communication. I actively encourage staff to touch the children as often as possible. I never pass a child without touching him or her; just a quick touch on the shoulder or arm, or a tousle of the hair, is enough to let the child know that you are around and in his life and that you want to be involved with him. We spend hours romping about on the floor, and in the pool several children come around me like flies round a jampot, waiting their turn to be thrown in, again and again. It is interesting that they always come to me; do they realise that, as the only man, I have probably got more strength than the ladies on the staff?

We do a tremendous amount of picture and object recognition in the nursery, the junior class and the senior class. We use pictures, we use the the real thing and the names of everyday things are repeated with monotonous regularity. Even if the child's language does not flow, we find tremendous strides made in the comprehension levels of most of the children. All details of every work session that every child has are written down on clip boards and then transferred to the teachers' records, so all progress and sometimes regression can be stated accurately.

I do not think it really matters one jot which line we take on the way through. Every assault on the child's senses is valid. Because the vast majority of stimuli enter our brains through our eyes and ears, there is a tendency to forget that we do in fact have three other senses to use. Touch is often ignored or kept to a minimum. We keep to our own little private space, and it is English people especially who do so. We meet a long-lost friend after several years and remain at two arms' length, which is the minimum needed to shake hands, rather than experience the joy of close physical contact with someone dear to us. We only rarely use our sense of smell, such as on occasions when aromas, scents and odours impinge on us more powerfully than usual. Even then, we tend to be negative and say things like, 'Cor! What a stink', as a diesel lorry fills our nostrils with fumes. But do we really savour the smell of flowers in the garden or the waft of fresh-baked bread coming from the shop as we pass? As for our sense of taste, it is probably our least used. Perhaps it has become jaded over the years because it has been eroded by the modern diet.

I actively encourage our children to use their minor senses. The messages going through the major receptors, the eyes and ears, do not make a great deal of sense to them, so if the other senses can help, why should they not be developed? Many autistic children sniff, mouth and tap objects and it is suggested that they are indulging in obsessional behaviour, but I am sure that they are investigating things like dogs do. Possibly the child is absorbing large amounts of information by seeing how things taste, smell and feel. We have had quite a few children who tap bits of jigsaw before putting them into place. Perhaps this tells the child which way up it goes. Stewart always sniffs objects before putting them in their right place. He washes up and then sniffs each item. Normally you would make a visual inspection of an item, but perhaps he sniffs them to see if they are clean. A dirty fork does have a particularly metallic tang to it. It is also common for visitors to get the once-over from some children as they arrive. It can be quite embarrassing for them to be sniffed and sometimes to have their clothes felt and licked, but the child must feel he needs to get to know them and this is his only way. There is obviously a limit to how far they can go, but it is a relatively easy matter to distract the child if he has gone too far and eventually he realises where the limits are.

Whenever we plan a programme for language and other communication skills we have to be very careful in plotting out what we are going to do. We have a full meeting and the class teacher takes notes of everyone's thoughts on the subject. We then have a composite picture of what we feel the child is capable of. This is vital, because even a simple instruction like 'look at me' assumes a tremendous amount. It presupposes that he understands 'look at' and, if he fixates on your shirt button when you give the instruction, then he has complied with your request. However, because eye contact is needed, it is perhaps better to ask the child to 'look at my eyes', although this again presupposes understanding of the word 'eyes'. When such apparently simple tasks involving language are analysed, we can see just how complex they are and it never ceases to amaze me how easily most people grasp them with little or no difficulty at all. With autistic children nothing can be taken for granted. It is only by dint of a totally concerted effort by the whole team that we can get anywhere. Everyone has to treat the child in the same way to achieve the high level of consistency the child needs to get anywhere at all.

The best example we ever had of the value of teaching a child to communicate his needs by any means that can be put at his disposal happened when Scott was in the pool one day. He was in difficulty, and as he went down for the third and final time, Alex, our most verbal child, pointed out to his teacher that 'Scott wants some help'. Scott was signing 'help' furiously, but at first glance he only seemed to be enjoying himself and thrashing his arms about. A visitor had once commented that it seemed unnecessary to teach sign language to speaking children. We did this simply so that they might be able to let us know if a signing child was trying to tell us something which we had missed. Thank goodness we had done it and thank goodness for the people who devised Makaton!

Although many of our children learn at least the fundamentals of communication, few become really fluent in the use of language; this means that only a few of them can exercise any great control over their environment through communication, leaving the majority dependent on a highly structured routine for their survival. It seems to give them a chance to know where they stand in life. However, continuing to give them too much structure can have its pitfalls. Everyone, handicapped or not, needs some structure in his life, but it is possible to go too far so that the routine becomes the only thing that matters. If the autistic child functions best within a highly organised routine and it is not provided, he falls down; but if the routine given to him only serves to make him even more devoted to set patterns, are we doing him any good at all? Are we setting a standard of routine at school that is far more organised than the one at home because there it is not quite so easy to arrange? The regime in the house must be more relaxed, because when the family are together they are usually at rest and in their free time. Each family member is doing his own thing, but the autistic child finds it difficult to occupy himself in what we would call a useful sort of way. So when the child goes home he may have to settle to a totally different routine and may find he cannot accept it; in this way, he may become more disruptive then ever. Have our efforts to teach him to settle into our routine therefore only served to make life more difficult for him?

Many questions need to be asked all the time about what we are actually doing for these children. We set out to achieve a level of stability and security, by having a drive on behaviour disorders and by trying to give the

Carmen, lost in her own world – the conventional image of the autistic child.

Total isolation.

'You will enjoy a tickle!'
Getting through to the child.

Communication is the most vital skill of all. A language session on the Language Master, which plays a word or sound and has the picture on the card.

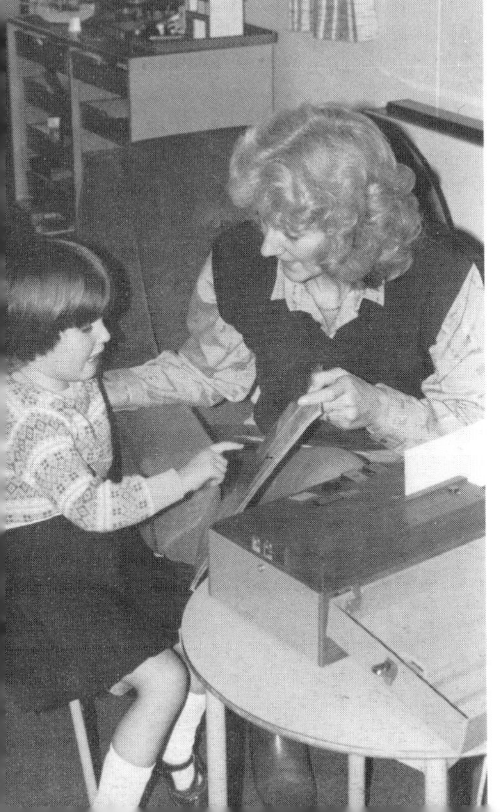

One to one language session.

Signing 'book' in Makaton.

Classwork, one to one.

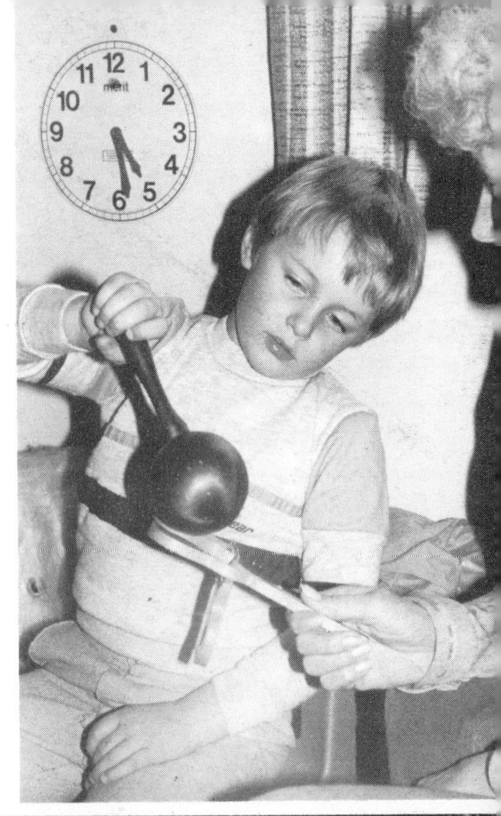

Learning rhythms, sometimes known as knocking seven bells out of the musical instruments!

Learning to match knives, forks and spoons. Such lessons should always be relevant to everyday living.

Matching letters as a precursor to reading.

Seeking help.

Bathtime should be fun.

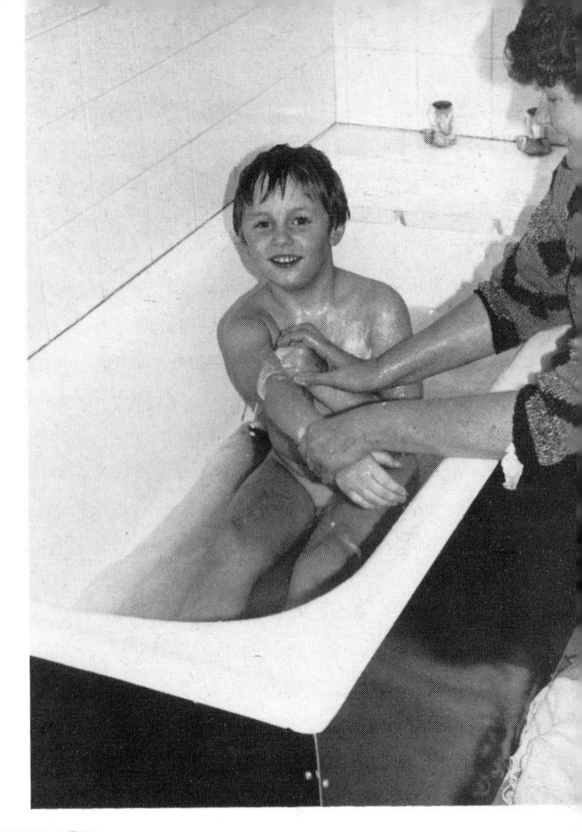

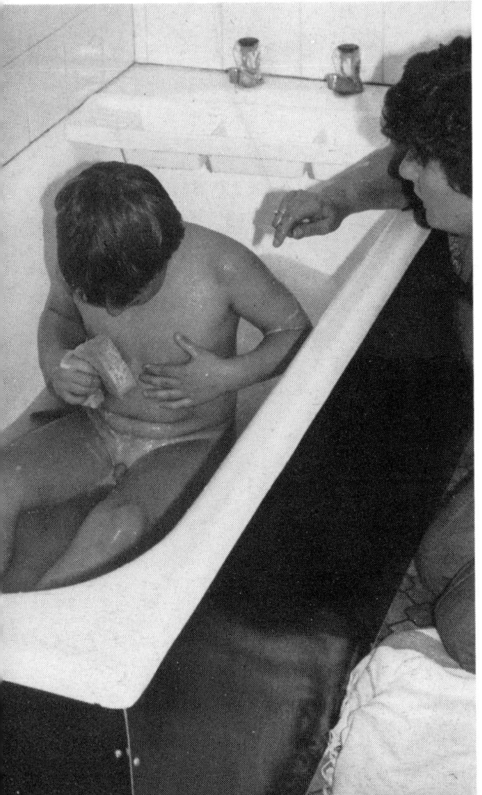

Learning to wash oneself.

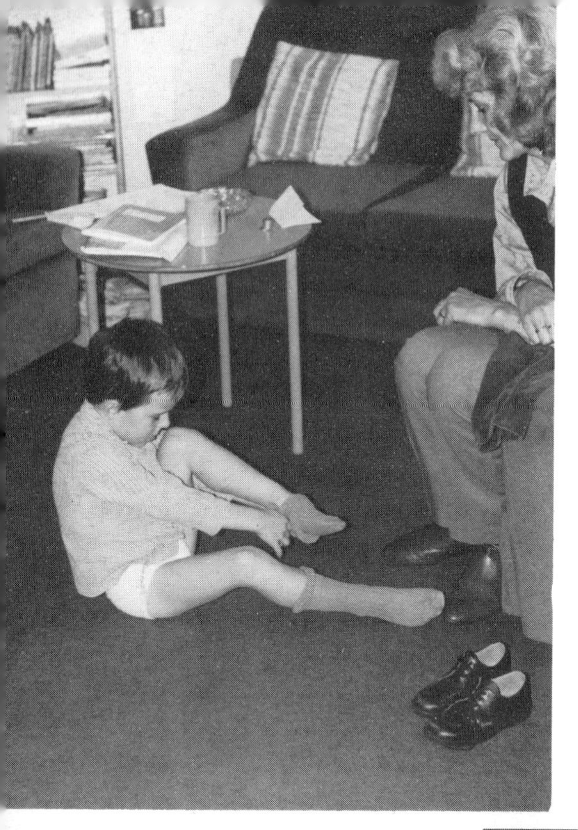

Learning independent dressing.

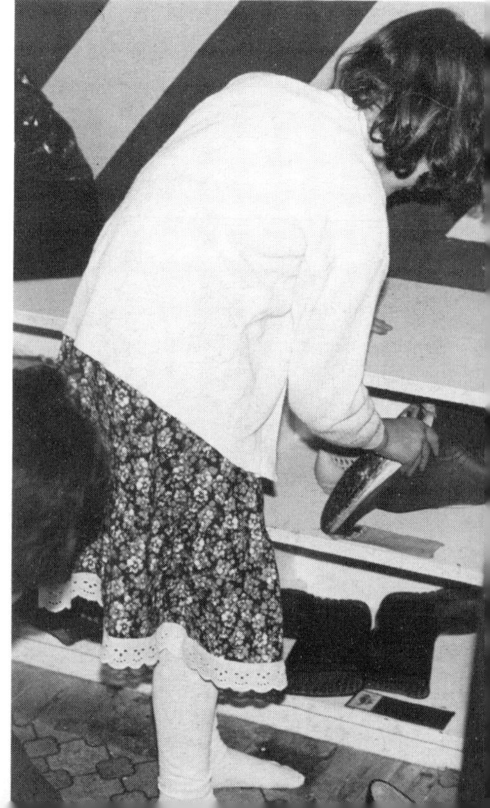

Learning to be tidy.

child a stable setting to function in, but even with the fullest co-operation with the home, which is what we strive for, and with the best will in the world, there is no way that we can expect a normal home to be as highly organised as school. Some families have tried to make their lives revolve around the child so that he can in fact have the routine he craves, but this goes totally against the normal social pattern where the children have to fit into the lifestyle dictated by the parents. The whole subject becomes very convoluted indeed and needs very careful analysis to avoid a situation where we finish up with children who are acceptable at school and remain very difficult at home, but who came to school in the first place because they were causing problems at home. We seem to have two choices. Do we try to persuade the parents to be as rigid as we are or do we alter our routines in an attempt to make the children more able to cope? These questions and many others like them occupy much of our staff meeting time because we are very keen to get the right balance. A system of continuous assessment is needed to avoid all the possible dangers of over-structuring.

Like all schools, we have our basic structure without which we could not function. There is a basic shell of a timetable. Meals are served at regular intervals, staff change shifts at fixed times and we have to stick to a set pattern for things that we do frequently, like when we need to go to outside activities such as horse riding and winter swimming at the Sports Centre. We need set times for the two classes to use the art room separately and there are rotas for the children to do their share of chores. The care staff also need rotas so that they get their fair share of difficult children.

Over the years I have decided that there are two distinct and separate types of routine that we need. The first is the individual routine in terms of how a child's behaviour problems are dealt with. In this routine the child learns what consistency is all about and hopefully comes to realise that things he does will always be treated in the same way. This means that his personal routine is rigid and fixed, but the other sort of pattern into which he must fit is that involving the whole group. We have gradually evolved a system that seems to suit everyone. We keep the basic pattern and then change things ever so gently but as much as possible within this basic framework. For example, we alter children's places at the table, we move beds around now and again, we go a different way to the stables, and, when we get there, a child may be made to ride a different horse. If he prefers to sit behind the driver in the minibus we persuade him to sit elsewhere and if he wants to ride a scooter round the playground in the same direction all the time, we suggest that he goes the opposite way. Slight changes like these are being made and accepted in the lives of children who were once reported by the parents to be limpet-like in their clinging to the same routine, day in, day out, and who at one time would go literally berserk if the tiniest thing changed. We have found that routine seems to lose its importance for many of the children and I feel that the need for this has been replaced by a feeling of security, trust and confidence. We have yet to find a reason why some children accept this better than others and so we have put it down to their different personalities, just as we would with non-handicapped children.

Occasionally a conversation between staff triggers off a full-blown discussion on the way in which we have treated the children. One such conversation got us exploring the possibility that we were over-programming the children like computers in our quest for an inflexible environment in which we felt they could best survive. A colleague commented that Jimmy seemed to do nothing without being told what to do. Another colleague spoke on the same theme. Jimmy had no language at all and, day after day, when he was washing his hands, for example, it had been assumed that he did not know what to do. So each step of the task had been put to him one by one and he must have automatically assumed that that is how you wash your hands. You put the plug in and wait to be told to turn on the tap. Then you wait to be told to turn it off again. We decided to try an experiment with Jimmy. The following day, after lunch, nobody told him directly to go out to play. The other children left and Jimmy stayed put. He was still there at tea-time, not getting upset, not doing anything, just waiting to be told what to do next.

This problem with Jimmy was easily overcome by removing all direct instructions and just giving him verbal encouragement instead. Rather than telling him what to do, we used expressions like, 'Yes, Jimmy, you know what to do', and it did not take him very long to realise what was expected of him. He was praised each time he did something right without our help and it may be my imagination that the look on his face was one of, 'It took you long enough to see where you were going wrong, didn't it?'

The following night gave us further insight into the way our children were performing like robots. The gas cooker was faulty and the cheese and potato pie was only half-cooked, so tea would be late. I was covering for an absent colleague and suggested that we should have seconds for firsts and then the pie when it was cooked. All twelve boarders came down to the dining-room and every single one of them devoured peaches and Carnation milk. They all used a knife and fork! Next day I raised the matter at a staff meeting to see if we could work out where things were breaking down. It was agreed that very few of our children were actually making any decisions in their lives unaided, and it was time to try to bring this to an end. We needed to know if this apparent lack of initiative was a consequence of the children's handicap and lack of linguistic skills, or if it was a product of our management techniques. There was only one way to find out and that was to try an experiment.

At breakfast-time the following morning the master plan was put into operation: no intercom message from the kitchen to say that breakfast was ready and no instructions from the staff, who sat there trying to force a conversation amongst themselves on any subject they could think of. As the clock ticked by, the result was exactly that which we had predicted—nothing at all! We sat and sat for forty-five minutes, and still nothing. Then Jane, who was still being toilet-trained, was taken for a regular 'potting' session. This prompted Alexander to ask if he could have some breakfast. He and I shot down to the dining-room where he promptly informed me that there was no toast. Instead of giving him detailed directions I merely told him that he had better do something about it. He stopped to think for a while, then went to the cook and asked for some toast. 'Certainly, Alex,' she said and handed him a plateful. He returned to his place grinning from ear to ear. Then he sat down and devoured the lot as if to say, 'I asked for it so I'll eat it'. Granted, he is our most able child as far as language is concerned, but it was a start and certainly a move in the right direction. That morning he was the only child to have any breakfast, apart from the much less able children who, we felt at that stage, were not capable of being able to think for themselves. Those we felt were capable were given Complan at breaktime to make sure they were not going without and we resolved to try the same thing the following morning.

We followed exactly the same routine and Alexander went down immediately to help himself to his breakfast. The rest sat like lemons, but we had a sense of some sort of agitation. Suddenly Claire, aged fifteen, began to cry. When asked what was wrong she signed 'food' and was told to go and get it, whereupon the tears stopped at once and she flew downstairs. Shortly afterwards, David decided that enough was enough and he, too, went down. He said, 'Sunday today', helped himself to a vast quantity of muesli and scoffed the lot. It struck me that he said this because at home it was probably more relaxed, as it should be, and he was perhaps not told to get his breakfast but was left to his own devices; hence his thinking it was Sunday. We could not let our children get their food when they simply felt like it, because we would have had an endless stream of children in the kitchen all day long; this would have blown our own routine and the cook's, and everyone in a school is aware that the cook is the ultimate power, never to be thwarted! We did feel, though, that we were at least moving in the right direction, to a situation where some of the children were starting to see the need to get food for the sake of eating and not just because someone told them to get it.

By 9.15 no more children had come down; then suddenly Sean must have felt hungry. He went to the dining-room where he sat for a good ten minutes. Then he took his cornflakes and sat again. He looked at one of the staff and began vigorously to sign 'milk' (which is symbolic of the milking of a cow by hand). The staff member simply gestured vaguely in the direction of the milk and turned away. Sean picked up the jug and helped himself, almost with a shrug as if to say, 'Ah, well, best I get on with it then'. As the days went by more and more of the children cottoned on to what was happening and, one morning, when I praised Alexander for his good thinking in passing the sugar bowl unprompted to Annabel, he said, 'I like thinking, I think.'

We have tried to apply this idea of 'free thinking' to other situations as well. It would not be wrong to assume that a non-handicapped child would apply the lessons learned in one situation to the next and, after a couple of examples of a system, would extrapolate enough from the first to be able to see a new pattern. Autistic children, even the more able ones, fail to do so because the ability to generalise needs a lot of language and with it the ability to think conceptually, so each situation needs to be 'taught in'. We began by stopping telling the children to do things in the self-care line. One very hot day, we did not tell them that there was no need for coats. Because we had programmed them to put their coats on there was no realisation of the when and the why of the situation. After ten minutes on the swing Claire, winter dressed with boots, gloves and thick coat, started to perspire heavily. She was asked if she was hot and she signed 'yes'. As soon as she was asked what she could do about it she whipped off her heavy clothes, returned them to her peg and came out smiling. We formed the impression that somehow all this free thinking was stemming from our lifting of all our rigid instructions and had been lurking under the surface as soon as we had got the children to understand and use even the smallest amount of language. We had concentrated so hard on the basics of communication, so that the children would be able to cope, and had finished up in a position where they only coped with what we had given them and no more. It was not an overnight change to get some of the children to be able to make choices and decisions on their own. It is much more of an on-going thing and every day we get more and more insight into the way our children's minds work.

As these sentences were being written, David was very upset about the fact that one of our ex-pupils was coming back to visit us with her parents. He categorically stated that 'she comes back, David's at home. She's a screamer!' We would never in a million years have dreamt of such a response from David when he first arrived. Whenever we can, we continue our line of positive encouragement as opposed to direct instruction. It does not work with all the children, of course; many of them still have to be told how to do things and cannot work things out for themselves.

We also see examples of children trying to get to grips with language and not quite getting there. One day Philip, aged 14, was told that it was his turn to wash up the morning drink cups in his classroom. He suddenly said, 'Don't want to'. His teacher was amazed and, convinced that he was really about to start to put his brain in gear, told him that he would not have to do them if he could tell her why not. He knew that a 'why' question needed an answer beginning with 'because' so he said, 'Because, because (long pause as he struggled with the combination of grammar and thought processes), because . . . I've got wax in my ears!!!!' He then sat back and grinned hugely, confident that he had got away with not washing up. Everyone was so delighted at the way he had tried so hard to win, that someone else washed up and he was very heavily 'Smartieised' and praised to the high heavens for using the little language he had to such brilliant effect.

It took a long time to evolve this very complicated system of building in communication skills and sorting out of routine, but we think we have eventually chosen the middle road so that those children who can cope with independence of differing degrees can be allowed to do so, while those who still seem to need a higher level of structure can have it. All the time we try to teach more and more language and communication skills; the whole school day revolves around trying to instil the skills which any child must have if he is to stand a chance of being able to function in a very difficult world. If, at the end of the day, it appears that we have only replaced one routine for living with another, at least we can argue that the new one is much easier for the child and his family to live with than the one we replaced.

7
OUR FAILURES

This chapter tells the story of three very different children who, in my opinion, are partial failures as far as the school is concerned. Martin had to leave and go into hospital, J.C. had to leave and go into a children's home miles from anywhere. They were both taken away by their Authorities against my wishes because their parents just could not cope any longer. Annabel is still with us at the time of writing, but her parents are coming to the end of their tether and we do not know what the future holds.

Martin's previous school was a private establishment, where the head's first comment to me was, 'Thank God, they're trying to place the little devil elsewhere, he's a bloody nuisance.' I went into Martin's classroom which held fifteen children and a teacher, a poor bewildered young thing who looked extremely embarrassed and harassed. The class consisted of fourteen Down's Syndrome children and Martin. As I walked in the teacher was talking about the colour of the day, asking the children if it was a green day or a pink day and if they could really feel the colour of the day . . . Martin was staring out of the window, flapping his hands and picking at the scabs on his fingers from previous self-mutilation sessions. The teacher's aside to me was, 'He doesn't talk, you see.' A few minutes later she clapped her hands and twittered, 'Right, children, number books.' Fourteen desks opened in unison, fourteen number books flew out and fourteen little Down's children began counting assiduously. Martin flicked and picked and added his own contribution: 'Pick up a blue one, you idiot,' and 'Bring on the Branston,' coupled with a vicious pinch on his immediate neighbour. Teacher: 'Oh, not again, Martin. Never mind, Tony, just move away.' Teacher's aside to me: 'You see, he can't count.'

Ten minutes later a clap of the hands brought out the musical instruments. Crash, tinkle and drum roll. Martin's ritualistic routine continued unabated. You can guess the aside this time: 'You see, he doesn't like . . .' and so it went on all morning. I repaired to the head's office where I was given a treatise on the value of handling balls of steel, silver and copper and the other intricacies of metal therapy. I left the place convinced of the well-meaning efforts of the staff on behalf of their charges, but equally convinced that Martin was totally unsuitably placed. If ever a child needed to be reorganised, here he was.

In retrospect, that school did more for Martin's family than it ever did for Martin. It was a seven-day placement, so he only had to go home at holiday times, but with us he would have to start going home every weekend as well, because we are only a five-day school. A long chat with his parents persuaded me that they wanted him home, loved him dearly in spite of the problems he created and felt that with our help they could cope—brave people. I have read that the relationship between parents and a handicapped child is often stronger than that in an ordinary family, but these people had real courage and I shall never forget how they were prepared to launch themselves anew into the fray and the torment that Martin would undoubtedly hurl at them.

As with all parents, I pointed out that he might be even worse for some time as he tried to sort out the whys and wherefores of the new constraints that would definitely be applied to him at Doucecroft. He had been through some twelve schools and each one had had to say, 'Sorry, we can't cope'. It did not take us long to see why his greatest positive points were his exceptional good looks, his mass of beautiful black hair, his enormous brown eyes and his day-brightening smile—he seemed to have no others.

Martin was totally incontinent. His mother admitted that she had had the most dreadful time trying to train him; he had sat on his potty for hours, screaming, yelling and generally causing mayhem, only to perform all over the floor as soon as she lifted him off. This apparently went on for years, with no success whatsoever.

This was probably Martin's worst feature, because lack of toilet-training is one thing which tends to render a child unacceptable. Double incontinence is revolting, especially in a child who has no apparent reason for being so, and particularly when he is no longer a baby, but eleven years old. It is no joke to have to deal with incontinence in a disabled paralysed person, but in this instance the carer can at least see why the problem exists; with the child who appears to be normal and therefore should be clean and dry, however, the situation for the carer becomes intolerable.

If Martin had simply continued to be dirty and wet he would have been enough for his family to bear, but he did not stop there. Many were the times he was seen to offer a fistful of his own faeces to staff, saying, 'Would you like it?'—guaranteed to make even the hardiest of staff blanch, especially at breakfast-time when they had just started an eight-hour shift; or, even worse, when the night staff had just finished a twelve-hour shift, having cleaned him up five times in the night, sometimes along with half a dozen other children. It was in fact at night that Martin came into his own. He smeared his excrement around, creating the most appalling mess. We had hardened night staff on duty, who could clean him up and say, 'Ah well, we finish at eight o'clock and it is part of the job, after all.' But try to imagine, if you can, the horrors for his family with carpets, bedding and curtains to clean night after night after night.

I can remember a social worker visiting the school one day when Martin was in full flight. She rattled on about family dynamics and the psychotherapeutic approach to the problem, but she failed totally to grasp my point that, whether we were faced with a problem created by the child or a problem created by the original family dynamics, either way the problem had to be overcome before anything could be done about altering the family. Eleven years of this treatment by Martin had the whole family on the verge of insanity, but the social worker insisted that we needed to sort out the parents first. I pointed out that a smashed-up car may possibly be the fault of a bad driver, but you need to repair his car before you can teach him better driving. She failed to see what I meant, so I persuaded her to leave and got down with my staff to the nitty-gritty—just how were we going to tackle what appeared to be an insurmountable problem?

A very long discussion took place at the next staff meeting. Records had to be checked for any reference to physical disorders. No such reference was found. The next stop was to request a total physical check on the child to see if anything had developed which might cause exceptional quantities of faeces. Nothing was found. The obvious line of approach was now leaning towards a programme of behaviour modification, but I stressed to my staff that the programme would have to be an extremely positive one, involving no sanctions or negative thoughts, because the family had admitted to doing nothing but play hell with him every time and this had only made matters much worse. The family also had to admit that their patience was so thin, they felt themselves totally unable to lavish praise on Martin if he ever was clean and dry, because he had effectively destroyed any of the caring side of the relationship. They had endured so much heartache with this lad that, although they loved him still, they found it impossible to do more than survive each day and express anger at the way he was treating them.

Both parents, however, insisted that with our help they would do their utmost to sort him out and do whatever we suggested, especially as their own efforts had totally failed. My first suggestion was that they should praise him if ever he managed to be clean. His mother had tried that ten years before and had given up; his father said he had never done it and would now start. We were now all agreed on the first principle. The second stage was to devise a programme of toileting.

We decided that the first hurdle to overcome was the establishment of a pattern, which up to now did not exist. Martin was to be 'potted' every twenty minutes; at the same time the word 'toilet' was to be used as often as possible, because Martin did not seem to have the vaguest idea of its meaning. If he performed correctly at any stage he was to be praised as lavishly as possible, however daft it might sound talking to an eleven-year-old as one would to a baby, and, perhaps more importantly, there was to be no sound or demonstration of irritation at all if the score was zero. The whole sequence was to be recorded faithfully on a chart to see if we could set out a pattern.

Within the space of a week we proved that Martin hated the toilet, had no idea of what to do in it, had no set times of performance, but did like being praised and certainly loved the idea of a Smartie if he did score a direct hit. One thing we never seemed to achieve was to get him to ask for the toilet when he actually wanted to go, although he often tried to use it as an escape from a situation he did not like. He would resist all efforts to get him to co-operate in a session of work in the classroom by shouting, 'Toilet, please.' He had probably sussed us out well enough to know that we would not refuse him this request in case he wet or dirtied himself. In spite of this, we did have some success during the day in that there was a marked reduction in Martin's double incontinence, but proof that he was only responding to prompting from us and was not actually toilet trained came with results at night: the success rate here can be described in one word—nil.

Martin continued to be filthy and soaked every night.

His normal routine was to chant things like, 'Oh the dirty little sod, he's done it again' and 'Do you like it?', or he used to sing his favourite TV jingles. 'Bring on the Branston' almost became the school hymn in those days. A visiting psychologist gave us a new tack to try in the behaviour modification field. It was a technique grandly termed 'restitution and overcorrection'.

The theory goes like this. An 'offence' is committed, so restitution has to be made, then further action by the offender has to be taken so that the situation finishes up even better than it was before the 'offence'. A simple example could be a situation where a child deliberately hurls his drink to the floor. He is made to clean up his drink (the restitution) and then he has to clean the whole floor, so that it is much cleaner than it was before he hurled his drink (the overcorrection). This approach in itself sounds reasonably simple, but it is also vital to do it the right way. The contact between the adult in charge and the offending child has to be absolutely minimal and as clinically detached as possible, so that the child receives no acclaim whatsoever.

In Martin's case the restitution involved his cleaning up his own mess, followed by his having to scrub the whole floor in his room. Unfortunately, the night staff spent more time trying to stifle their giggles as Martin churned out his repertoire while scrubbing frenetically round his room. He used to grit his teeth and grind out the words: 'There, I suppose you're happy now', 'Oh, God, look at this', etc., etc. Obviously not funny for his parents, but we have found out over the years that laughing about the horrors facing us is a very good way of keeping our sanity. Coupled with the overcorrection was a daytime programme of cleaning which was done in an extremely light-hearted way, with as much physical contact as possible and heaps of praise lavished freely as Martin completed each task. The theory was that he would realise that the only time that cleaning things could be enjoyable was if he was clean himself, and that cleaning up his own mess was boring and not fun in the least.

Now, I knew the theory and so did the theorists and my staff. Martin should have twigged as well and started to see the light. He did not. Any attention at all was better than none. He did not mind what happened and the technique was abandoned. Another approach was called for. If we could find some way of preventing Martin getting near his faeces with his hands, perhaps he would get fed up with the idea of smearing his floor and walls so liberally. One of my night staff was married to a merchant banker who had a spare pin-stripe shirt. Such wonderfully long tails and sleeves! The sleeves were stitched together and the shirt was slipped over Martin's head. It was like a very long nightshirt with the sleeves like a muff from which he could not remove his hands. This meant that Martin might still be able to soil himself, but he would not be able to play with the stuff and therefore might tire of the whole thing and give up after a few nights of this prevention.

The first night he was dirty but had not smeared it around; the second night the same result; the third night, hey presto! clean; the fourth night clean; the next night filthy and, instead of handprints, footprints. Obviously our young friend had mastered Newton and his law. If it comes down it comes out, so all he needed to do was to stand up in bed, soil himself and out it came, ready to be paddled in and trodden round the room. I suppose once you get the hang of things it's quite fun, really. We never did crack this problem.

I suppose it sounds as if Martin was a very unlikeable sort of lad, but the truth is that we all thought the world of him and wanted desperately to alter his ways, if not for him, then for his family. Martin also suffered severe epilepsy and his fits were scarcely contained by drugs; the poor lad often keeled over and we had to get the doctor in to stop his often prolonged fits. As he came round he would look extremely frightened and panic-stricken, but then as soon as he recovered he would start his usual tricks.

As well as his favourite activity, chronicled above, Martin had other leanings. He was obsessed with light switches, which he flicked on and off as often as he got the chance. We attempted to cure that by making, or trying to make him count them. A member of staff would walk around the school with him to try to get him to count the switches. If he repeated the numbers correctly, he was allowed to switch one light on. The next step was to get him to touch, say, two switches consecutively, after which hc was allowed to turn one on. This could, eventually, with a more compliant child, have led to some rudimentary comprehension of number value, but in his case it only served to make him angry as soon as he was stopped. We actually did succeed in one main area. We managed to get Martin to sit down to eat at a table, and although he remained very loud, we did seem to get through to him a little with food. Any response had to be immediate. It was useless to threaten to withhold food some time later, but removal of his meal for unacceptable behaviour often calmed him down rapidly, and so meal-times became much more pleasant with him and for him.

Sad to say, Martin's treatment of his family finally caused them to crack. They realised that his case was uncontainable and their local Education Authority had to place him in a subnormality hospital in his own county. It broke his parents' hearts to do it, but they had to consider themselves and their other two children as well. I saw Martin two years later, in 1983. The staff in the hospital reported that he was still dirty, still aggressive to himself and to other people, that he continued to pinch their arms viciously, yelling 'Did that hurt you?' and 'Do you like it?' at the top of his lungs, but when I saw him in action, the beautiful smile was gone, the eyes were empty and he did not even seem to enjoy hurting people. If only we had been open a few years earlier, we could perhaps have done a lot more for him and with him. I still do not feel that Martin was one of our failures. The system is such that there was nowhere for him to go at weekends to give his family a rest and there was no one in their area who could offer practical advice on how to handle him and how to keep the continuity with school, which is of paramount importance for all these children. We were able to offer advice through the weekly report book, but they needed someone to be there and somewhere to send him now and again. The system has many flaws but it is all we have for now. If Martin was the victim of anything, perhaps he was a victim of 'the system'.

* * *

Another child whom I consider to have been a similar tragedy was J.C. He was our first pupil and, as I have already mentioned, he disappeared into the toilet as soon as he arrived. Once I had prised him from the toilet we had to try to organise him. We had to show him his new bedroom and get his clothes unpacked. Like it or not, he was to stay with us each week and would not be going home for five long days, days in which, for the first time, he was going to try to start the long, painstaking process of learning to live in a group without being totally in charge. We also had to teach him basics such as what each room was, who people were, what their roles were, who the other children were, and a myriad other trivia. All this turmoil can be horrendous enough in the life of any child, but for J.C. it was an impossible task. Compared with Martin he was certainly not so far gone, and indeed had a fair amount of language. This was very limited, but he could express some of his needs and wishes. Like all our speaking children, his scope for language was always limited to concrete statements and he was unable to express concepts. However, J.C. at least had the groundings and this made him easier to get through to.

J.C. had been to an autistic unit in his Local Authority,

but the teacher there admitted that the Authority was only paying lip-service to a demand from the then Secretary of State for Education for each Local Authority to declare what provision was made or to be made for autistic children. The teacher, cynical in the extreme (and who can blame her?), was promised the earth in this 'pioneering venture' and given a room in a derelict school, one nursery nurse assistant and six children, all rather disturbed and all more limited than J.C. He had ruled the roost here for eighteen months, but his parents had been unable to cope with him on a day-to-day basis; so it was that J.C. was put forward to me, underwent the due processes of 'assessment' and, several months later, finished up in our toilet.

J.C. had extremely low levels of tolerance, which was hardly surprising. He could take very little pressure at a time and, as soon as he reached his tolerance level, he began to get very upset. He started off by crying and waited for the response. He had had ten years of getting his own way, which was his parents' way of keeping the peace, and obviously expected the same response. If it failed to come, he then went through a process of self winding-up which began with face-slapping, then self-scratching and pinching which usually culminated in vicious head-banging. At this juncture we decided that the first approach to head-banging was to ignore him totally. The minute the head-banging started, the member of staff involved with him would turn her back on him and pay attention to another child. We noted his reaction over a two-week period and timed the length of each outburst. As ever, everything was written down in detail, ready for discussion at the next staff meeting. The ignoring technique failed: there was no reduction at all. Check variables first. Were all staff doing exactly the same thing? Yes. Was there any pattern to the self-injury apart from frustration and an attempt to escape from the scheme? No. New approach called for. It was decided to try a technique which has attracted some gasps of horror over the years, but I always argue that unorthodox children require unorthodox treatment, especially those children who have failed totally to respond to conventional education.

This new approach was very straightforward. Every time J.C. banged his head he was to be told to do it again. The theory behind the approach was as follows. J.C. would be shocked. He would have his most powerful weapon, that of manipulation, removed and he himself would start to be manipulated by us. He would get fed up with not being in charge by use of this 'skill' which he had developed into a fine art over the years. He would stop and think, perhaps for the first time in his life, that there was every possibility that he could begin to enjoy the activities we were trying to get him to do.

As with so many unusual approaches, you are in fact flying by the seat of your pants. So many different ways have been tried and they have all failed, so you take a flying chance that another way, thought out as carefully as possible beforehand, but without a guarantee of success, may be the answer. Of course, it must be very carefully monitored and supervised, so that a snap decision can be made as to whether it should continue or end at any given moment. Whatever the reasoning behind it all, the first time I told J.C. to bang his head again had a startling result. He stared at me in disbelief, smashed his head against the wall and sobbed his heart out. The next time he hesitated, then banged his head. The third time he cried and said, 'No thank you'. We had virtually no more head-banging from J.C. for the rest of his stay in school.

You may recall an earlier reference to J.C.'s keenness on locks. At some stage, for reasons best known to himself, he had found a fascination in keys and locks. An obsession is only acceptable if it does not block other learning activities and if it does not become a nuisance to everyone else. In J.C.'s case it was doing both. If he got hold of keys it was the devil's own job to get them from him and his parents were driven to distraction by his desire to fiddle with them. They also found it very difficult to tolerate his habit of locking doors at the most inconvenient times, such as when he was indoors and they were outside. We decided that this in itself was a problem that needed tackling, but J.C. had another fancy which was perhaps even more important: he was able to unscrew doorknobs with remarkable ease. He used to get the knob off and then hurl it into the room, slam the door behind him and laugh his socks off. Access to the room was then blocked until I took off another doorknob and used it in place of the one he had removed. It was not just a question of putting his doorknob back in place of mine, because in a three hundred-year-old building there is likely to be a multitude of different doors and very few knobs were a match. Each incident involved a lot of work for me and, with thirty-one doors, all I could see stretching before me was a career of doorknob replacement.

When I was ten my father hit on a behaviour modification technique to stop me smoking. He could have chosen the negative therapy approach (a good thumping), or the withdrawal of reward technique (cancellation of pocket money, perhaps), or even the time-out approach (kicked up to bed), but instead he chose the satiation or flooding technique. Naturally he never once stopped to apply the above titles to what he did; he just called it common sense. The flooding technique could also be called the sickening technique, because he persuaded me to smoke ten of his very strong fags one after the other. With glee I began, but my glee vanished as the smoke took over. I spare your sensitivities by glossing over the results of the experience, but I never smoked again until I went to college.

We decided to apply the same approach to J.C. After a staff meeting I took the lad to his bedroom and gave him a screwdriver. I told him to take the doorknob off, which he did with pleasure. Then he had to replace it. He thought he was in his element as we proceeded to the next door and repeated the operation. The process went on all day, for a total of seven hours; I was bored, tired and cheesed off, but unfortunately J.C. was almost trembling with pleasure. So the next day the process was repeated. I should add that my staff were keeping me plied with plenty of coffee, and deliberately made comments about the fact that they were bringing me a lovely drink, but that J.C. would have to wait for his. In this way he might see that the current activity was not being done for fun. Day two ended with a total of doorknobs, removed and replaced, fast approaching the hundred mark and J.C. was showing no signs of flagging; having started, however, I felt it necessary to continue to the bitter end. Perhaps I should have had us sponsored! After nine days he started to show signs of giving up and half-way through day ten he opened a window, posted the screwdriver through it and said in a very plaintive way, 'No more, thank you.' From thereon J.C. never, to our knowledge, fiddled with another doorknob.

We have very often seen one obsession take over from another and, if this does happen, you either find yourself back to square one with an equally unacceptable obsession or, if things go well, with an obsession that is more tolerable and possibly even usable. In J.C.'s case we were lucky. He suddenly showed himself to be very keen on numbers and, without any help from us, began to do very complex computations in his head. He could calculate seventeen times twenty-nine at amazing speed, but had no idea at all of the meaning of numbers, although we were able to teach him the values of one to ten. He was able to transfer this to the serving of drinks, by counting the numbers of children and staff in the room; he was able to set tables by counting out the appropriate numbers of cutlery; and he finished up with his greatest achievement, going to the shop alone to buy a Mars Bar and returning with the correct change. His number thing only carried him away a few times, such as when the night staff caught him at two o'clock one night, with his bed stripped, a blue crayon in hand, numbers written all over the sheet, and he himself pointing to the next child, sound asleep. 'Peter did it,' he intoned. The staff burst out laughing, he joined in and could not wait until breakfast the next day to drag me upstairs to show me his deed.

As the months went by, J.C. became a very reliable member of our community. His language remained very superficial, and it was always impossible to hold anything but the briefest conversation with him; but he could be relied on to carry simple messages, he could do useful tasks like washing up and helping with the cleaning, and generally he seemed quite happy. Unfortunately, another obsession reared up. J.C. became very interested one day in the London Underground. We never found out why or how, and in fact in school it was only restricted to the theory. He would spend literally hours of his free time writing the names of all the tube stations on each line in turn. It seemed a harmless enough pastime and we actually encouraged it, as a way to help his memory and his language, and he seemed to derive a lot of pleasure from communicating with us. However, from home we received a report that J.C. had decided to apply the practical side as well. He had disappeared from home on the Saturday morning, found his way to the tube, bought a ticket with money found at home and ended up in Regent Street. Unfortunately he could not find his way home and started to get very upset. Startled passers-by called the police who managed to get his name and address from him. They took him home to his accompaniment of 'policeman, policeman' and 'nick, nick' and the scene was set for trouble. Over the next half-term J.C. frequently disappeared into London. His parents tried to lock him in the house, but that only caused ructions and, each time he got the chance, he ran away.

He was returned several times by the police and then one day he was arrested by a store detective. His old love of keys and locks resurfaced and he was caught helping himself to pocketfuls of them in a large London superstore. The police were called and they decided to charge him, probably because he looked so normal. He was left in the interview room and panicked. He went berserk and smashed up a chair and desk. His 'punishment' was to receive a caution from a senior police officer who came to school in full uniform and laid the law down. J.C. loved it and the whole thing fell on very stony ground.

His parents were very upset by the whole experience and were advised by the police to keep him in, but that was easy to say. All this time J.C. was very settled at school, but we could only guess at the terrible problems which we were told were developing at home. Every time J.C. came home he wanted to go out, but his parents had to stop him. He gradually reverted to his old habit of banging his head and slapping his face viciously, and then began to be very aggressive to his parents. Eventually I began to see signs that things were getting out of control again at home and, not long afterwards, his father rang to tell me that J.C. 'had to go'. Their Local Education Authority hastily arranged a transfer to 'some place in another county' and we never saw J.C. again. I have seen his family a few times since and they assured me that their lad was all right, but I would love to see him again to check for myself. We often talk about him at school and wonder if we could have straightened him out, but, just like Martin, he was well on his way to being a teenager when he came to us. If only we had been around when he was three . . .

* * *

Annabel was one of the new children in the second term. The only word to describe her accurately was 'spitfire'. At the age of eight she was totally out of the control of her parents and just did her own thing all the time. Her parents had tried desperately hard to sort her out but, as so often happens, they had had virtually no advice or help. She had an older brother and sister whose early years had been devastated by their severely handicapped sister. One of the worst things about Annabel was that she would not allow anyone within an arm's length of her and, if they approached beyond that boundary, she would literally attack them with all the means at her disposal, fair or foul.

Everyone who knew her before she came to us had learnt this lesson the hard way and they kept as far away from her as necessary to avoid being attacked. We could see exactly why within a very short time, as various members of staff took the brunt of her attacks. We chose a programme of 'touch and back off quickly' which involved touching her on the shoulder and getting away as quickly as possible before she could react. The hope was that she would get used to our touching her but realise that we meant no harm. The second stage was to be touching her more obviously and for longer and longer, with the final objective of being able to put an arm round her and ultimately giving her a cuddle.

This seemed like a good, positive approach and sounded easy. We could surely touch and skip away before she could get us, or so we thought. The first time I deliberately touched her she had her fingernails in my hand and her teeth in my shoulder before I could move. Over many years she had learnt that to get rid of people, who no doubt terrified her, all she had to do was go for them like a ton of bricks. The reaction she had always received had proved this to her time after time. Rule two was then applied. We had to unlearn her previous opinions and force her to accept our proximity because, unfortunately, she had to see that life consists of other people being near us. Rule two was as simple as the first stage but was to prove a lot more dangerous. If she reacted more quickly than you did and she went for you, she had to be grabbed and wrestled into a hold that she could not break. If she calmed down quickly, great, but if not, so be it. She had to be gripped as firmly as possible for however long it took her to stop the struggle.

The first time we tried it she attacked. The girl who got stuck with her had only worked with us for three days; she had been told the plan and how to cope with it. She had touched Annabel's shoulder in passing and had said, 'Hello, Annabel'. She was only one tenth as quick as she needed to be and she really got it in the neck, literally. She tried to get a grip of Annabel and failed first time. By the time she had a good hold her face was bleeding from the scratches and she had been bitten three times. She eventually got a tight hold and pressed her head hard against Annabel's. Not hard enough, it seemed, because she was given an almighty head butt in the mouth and her lip was split. Any sane person would have done exactly what Annabel expected, but this girl, being new, must have been trying to impress me. She shook the tears from her eyes and gripped harder. Next minute she let go of Annabel's hand to try to get a better hold and, for her trouble, received an almighty smack in the breast, which I believe is as painful as a kick in the nether regions for a man.

Annabel fought like a tiger, but gradually she seemed to begin to weaken. My colleague relaxed with her and immediately Annabel started again, almost as if she had relaxed on purpose to instil a false sense of security in the person she considered to be her tormentor. She renewed her attack and struggle with great frenzy, but after an hour and ten minutes she finally gave up the battle. Child and adult were soaked in sweat and Annabel flopped to the floor. At last, a win, and the winner went off to the staffroom to recover and have a fag or three. Half an hour later she went back into the classroom and took another dose, because Annabel was just behind the door and she got too near again. This time she suffered another twenty minutes of the same treatment.

Over the next three months, every single member of my staff received the same sort of punishment, but we all knew that if we failed to make Annabel accept us near her without a battle, then she would have to go, finishing the rest of her life in a hospital somewhere, probably restrained in a chemical straitjacket. As the weeks passed she seemed to be a little more tolerant of us, although she still went mad when she considered us to be too near. The battles grew shorter and shorter and she even accepted our touches more and more. One day, we finally got through from breakfast to teatime without any trouble at all. I stayed late that evening because there were two staff off sick. I was on duty in the playroom and was sitting trying to play with one of the children. Annabel was sitting quietly at the far side of the room, when she suddenly let out an almighty squeal and shot across the room towards me. The other children scattered and I slipped off my spectacles in case she smashed them. In that brief moment I was convinced that death was imminent. However, Annabel stopped within a foot of me, turned her back and flung herself onto my lap. She grabbed my hands, clapped them onto her sides, manipulating my fingers and saying 'too-too' repeatedly. This was the first time we had seen her approach anyone voluntarily, the first time she had been heard to speak. I tickled her, she laughed. I tickled her again, she laughed like a drain. I continued to tickle her, she continued to laugh, I was enjoying it, she got carried away with it and wet herself! I had a lecture that night, straight from school, and the ladies I spoke to could not understand why I was happy to be wet.

Apart from a few periods of upset, which we used to put down to the weather or just the way she felt in herself, Annabel remained calm and amenable for a couple of years. She was learning quite a few things. She could write her name, although we never really knew if she understood it. She could count reliably if she was relating the counting to something meaningful like sorting out cutlery to set the tables. She could be trusted to do this without much supervision and enjoyed washing up. Now and again she would flare up when she felt pressurised, but she soon calmed down again with a sharp word. Very rarely, her old aggression came to the surface, when she would pinch a staff member or another child, but it was finished as soon as it started and, generally speaking, she was nice to be with in school.

At home it was often a different story. Annabel had many weekends when she was quite settled; but there were other times, particularly in the holidays, when she tried to dictate the pace to the family. They found her very demanding and I think that they were so concerned about her regressing to the spitfire of old that they could not steel themselves to dominate her. I admire them for even having faced alone those first years of her life, when their lovely little girl put them through hell on earth, and they need a medal for tolerating so much. She was much better than she had been, but was far better at school. Perhaps she knew staff less well, perhaps she knew that staff had a chance to go home to recharge their batteries every day and could therefore cope better with her than her family could. There was also a chance that she was more fully occupied at school and, again, that is hardly surprising. It has happened time and time again that we have coped better with the children than the parents, because we can give them a day that is more full, without having to think about anything else, like Dad's tea or the other children in the family.

When Annabel's puberty hit her she changed dramatically. She went downstairs with the other children for breakfast one morning as usual and, instead of going into the dining-room, planted herself inside the front door. Our first tactic was to see if she would eventually get fed up and go in search of food. She did not, so I told her to go to the dining-room. She rounded on me like a wild thing and we were back to square one. This seemed to be getting us nowhere, so we had a rapid staff meeting to discuss what to do next. We decided that, in the first instance, we would push her as far as the dining-room and demand that she eat whatever was put in front of her. The first two mealtimes it worked. She was pushed by two people together to the dining-room, where she sat to eat as usual. Then she allowed herself to be pushed there but refused to eat. A day later she seemed to be determined to do one thing and one thing only: to plant herself either at the front door or in any corner she came to.

I called in a friend who is a clinical psychologist because, never having experienced this before, we were totally at a loss as to what we could do. This friend devised a programme of several stages. First, Annabel had to be told to walk. If that did not happen, she was to be told to walk, followed by being asked if she wanted a slap. If that failed, stage three was to repeat the first two and raise a hand in a gesture of a slap. Then a slap was added to the list. If that failed, she was to be carried unceremoniously to the dining-room and deposited in her place, where it would be demanded that she eat. If she failed to eat she was to be made to, however severe the battle. Obviously, if at any stage of the programme she responded, she was to be praised emphatically. It took six weeks of this programme to restore the status quo, but the interesting thing was that this very complex and distorted child actually 'undid' the programme. She co-operated at each stage by eating first, then by walking to the dining-room after a slap, then after the hand gesture, then after the verbal suggestion of a slap and, finally, when told to walk. Those six weeks were very trying for us but they must have been even worse for Annabel.

Annabel's next 'thing' followed soon after. She became a child of extremes. Every movement became very rapid and then it would become almost 'action-replay' slow. She began to use reams and reams of toilet paper, or she tore tiny squares off each sheet and tried to use those, with filthy hands as a result. She would then wash her hands in two seconds flat or she would scrub them compulsively until they began to be red-raw. She ate like a sparrow, putting tiny, tiny portions of food in her mouth and spending literally hours over a meal, or she would cram vast quantities of food into her mouth until she made herself vomit. She would either try to down a beakerful of drink in one mouthful or she would sip it for hours, a drop at a time. Funny walks started, where she tried to follow all the lines on a patterned floor, or she would try to walk everywhere in straight lines, even barging into furniture to achieve her objective. One minute she was walking around with her eyes staring wide open and the next she had them tightly closed. She either slept solidly and was nearly impossible to wake, or she did not sleep at all. One day she would ask for the toilet fifty times and pass a tiny drop each time, the next she would hold her water for over twenty-four hours at a stretch and then nearly flood the place out.

There seemed to be little that we could do about it. As soon as she was told to stop one activity she went to the other end of the scale. The minute you told her to stop rushing, she would slow to a crawl. When you told her to stop crawling, she rushed off into the distance. We decided that the only thing we could do was to have a member of staff with her at all times to encourage her to do the right things, to prevent her physically from doing wrong things and to look for good things she did, so that we could praise her.

Again, all these funny mannerisms died away as rapidly as they had come and the next thing was far less worrying but unbelievably irritating. Annabel suddenly started to copy everyone's actions. If a member of staff sat cross-legged, she did the same. If one changed legs, so did Annabel. She copied the slightest movement that anyone made. If you told her to go away, she went on to the next person and copied her instead. One day she sat behind five staff sitting on a bench and copied each one of them in turn. We suddenly stopped this weird behaviour by ourselves copying her. If she copied my hand position, I would wait for her to do something else then follow her round, copying whatever she did. We all did this for a week and she gave up only to replace it with manic giggling or bouts of crying for no reason that we were able to ascertain. There was precious little difference in the sounds and you would have the impression that she was crying, only to turn and see her laughing, apparently at nothing. We began to wonder if she was having hallucinations, but as she had no use of language she could not tell us if she was seeing things or not.

This phase disappeared as soon as the others and the next stage was a period of quiet, in which she seemed to be in a trance all the time; this, however, was very short-lived and she soon began to respond to us. She began to appear to enjoy life again and she started to enjoy cooking. At one time, at home, she would go into the kitchen whenever she had a chance and make vast quantities of food, such as spaghetti bolognaise; she would either eat it all and make herself sick, or she would pour the whole lot down the waste disposal unit. Now, at school she was really into doing things properly. She learned, and is still able, to make superb cakes, and her Yorkshire pudding is the envy of all the staff, especially the cook. She has spent a lot of time with the cleaners and has learnt to use a vacuum cleaner with precision. She can now be left to clean the whole playroom with the minimum of supervision and appears to enjoy the praise she gets for doing so.

Annabel is now an easy child to manage because she is so much quieter and she seems to want to do things that are offered to her. She suffers terrible PMT and is often bad-tempered when it starts. We make allowances for it and try to anticipate any trouble, which at worst results in her slamming down her plate or a cup on the table for no apparent reason. She is told off and the incident is closed. Annabel is definitely a child who seems to need to stick rigidly to a routine and finds it very difficult to accept changes. She cannot cope with the dramatic change from school to home each week and at times she still makes life exceptionally difficult at home, although this is better than it used to be, when she made life hard all the time. Her parents are finding themselves less and less able to cope. Annabel continues to be a lonely sort of girl and is probably at her best when left alone. Unfortunately, life consists of more than this. It is odds on she will need care for life and this is our priority for her future. We have to ensure that there will be a place for her, although this will not be very easy. She is now in her mid-teens and will have to leave us at the age of nineteen, because the law says that handicapped children are not entitled to education beyond that age. We have our fingers crossed and so do her parents.

8
THE NURSERY UNIT

During the first five years of the school, I gradually came to the very firm conclusion that many of the problems resulting in some of our children failing to 'make the grade' and having to be removed arose because we were not able to take them young enough. The arrival of the 1981 Education Act gave a lot more chance for the parents of handicapped children to obtain suitable education for their children at the age of two. This presupposed the availability of such provision. I felt quite certain that the Local Authority would jump at the chance to have a nursery facility especially as the '81 Act was putting children forward for Special Education at a much earlier age.

Although there is not a lot of positive evidence that a child taken early will be any better off than one taken later, it strikes me as obvious that the sooner the pressure is lifted from the parents the better things must be. It would be very difficult to find a family who would not readily swap thirteen years of hell and torment for a lesser sentence of three years or so.

With all this in mind, I put my ideas to the committee in 1982 and was well pleased with the response. The first suggestion was that I should test the water with the Local Authority and, as I guessed, they were very keen. The next hurdle was to get planning permission and then I had to deal with that other trivial matter, the question of finding the pennies. The planning permission was a long time coming, because Kelvedon is a conservation area and Doucecroft is a grade II listed building. This meant that it was important that the nursery unit I envisaged, a flat-roofed, single-storey, demountable classroom, should not detract from the visual aspect of the general scene. It took a lot of talking and presentation of scaled drawings to prove that the building would be almost invisible to passers-by, that it would be painted in suitable rural colours and that the safety of our children would be of paramount importance. One councillor objected on the grounds that passengers on passing buses would have their eyesight offended by the view, but it was pointed out to her that all the buses passing through Kelvedon were single-deckers. After lengthy debate in similar vein, the planning committee finally cracked. The financial aspect looked like being a severe headache. There was no chance of any help from the Education Authority because their budget had already been allocated to paying the fees for up to five children and, since their budget is permanently over-stretched, there was no way that they could even be approached for capital expenditure assistance.

With this in mind, I decided to hold some sort of function to raise funds, but what on earth could I do to get about £10,000 in a short time? This little problem apart, I looked through my list of contacts, of people and organisations willing in the past to donate raffle prizes and the like, and proceeded to ring Great Universal Stores in London. At this juncture serendipity smiled upon me. The art of getting lucky by chance does not often happen in a lifetime, but this time I struck paydirt with a vengeance. The girl on the switchboard happened to put me through to what appeared to be a wrong number. The girl who answered the 'phone said in a very cheerful voice, 'Good morning, Wolfson Foundation. Can I help you?'

Now anyone in the fund-raising game should know that the Wolfson Foundation was founded by the Wolfson family who own Great Universal Stores. In for a penny, in for a pound, I thought, and told the young lady what

One way of learning independence.

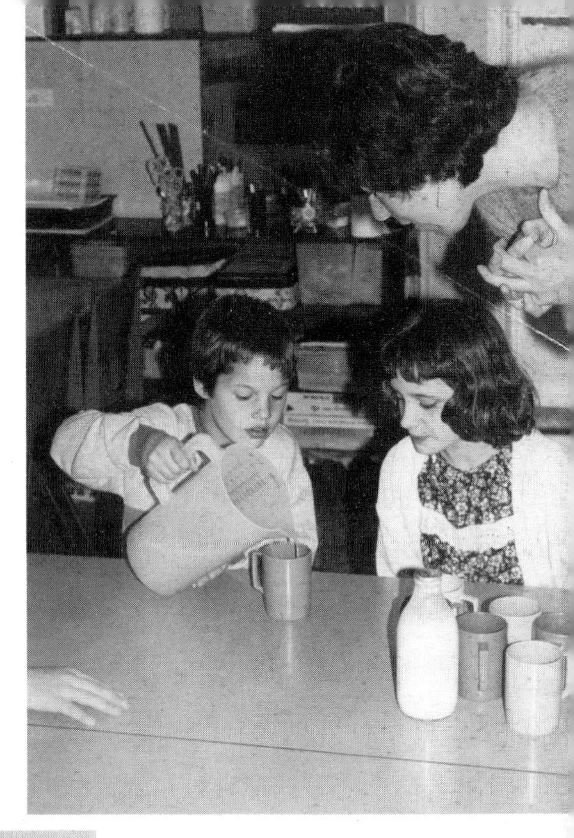

Cookery lessons are a popular part of the curriculum.

Lunchtime in the nursery. Note the snapshots on the wall, so that every child can learn to recognise him- or herself.

Lunchtime in the main school.

Tranquillity after the meal.

Learning to share the household routine.

Even the tinies have jobs to learn.

One to one in the pottery room.

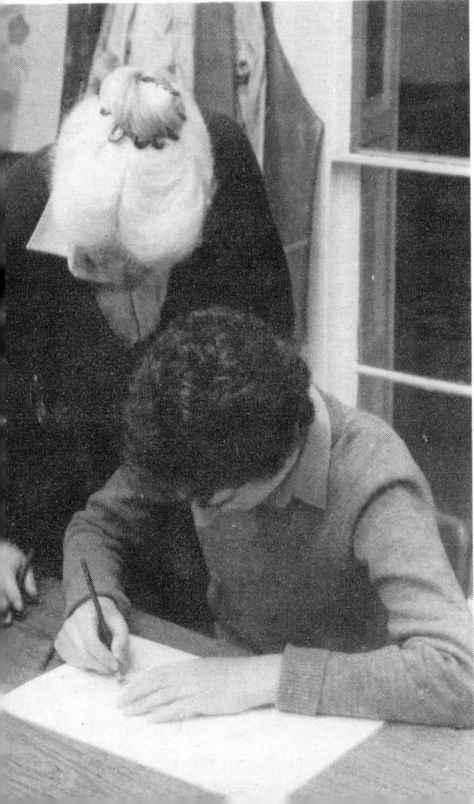

Deep concentration in the art room.

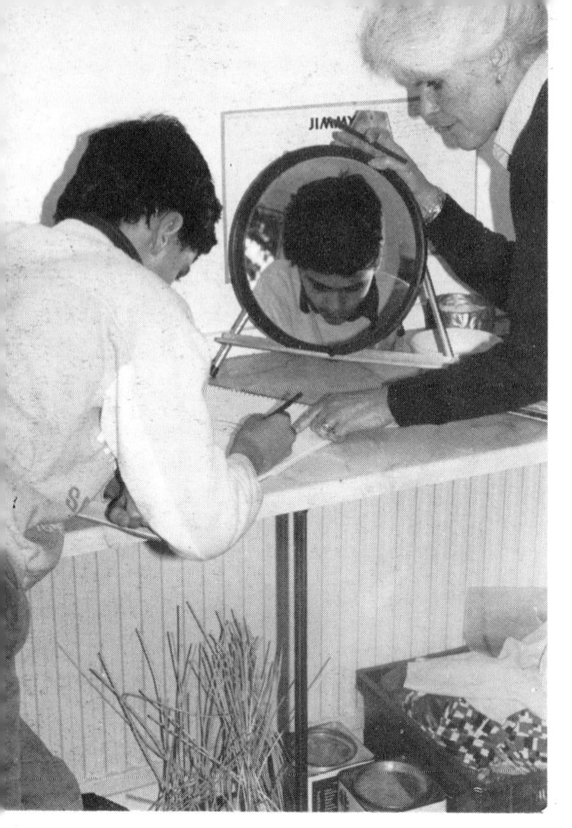

Self awareness from a self-portrait.

Working independently in the garden.

Free time normality.

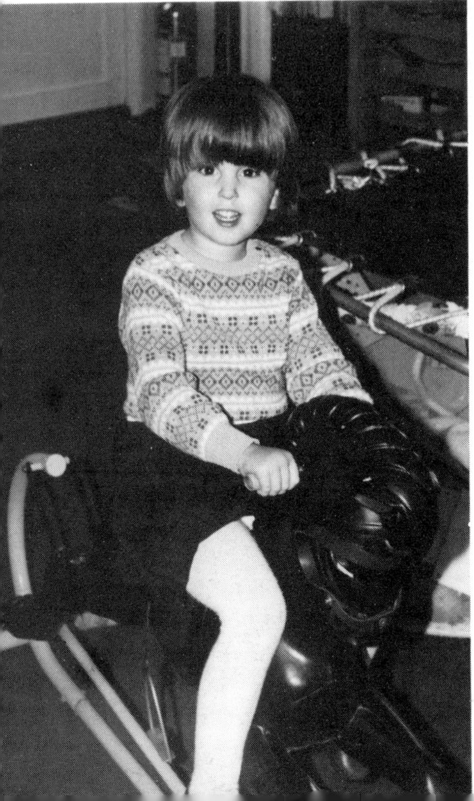

Playtime in the nursery.

Pretending to enjoy being on horseback – most children come to love riding once they have overcome their initial anxiety.

our plans were. She told me to write in with full details, plans, quotations and any other relevant information. I crossed my fingers, toes, eyes and everything else and hoped and prayed for a thousand pounds or so. Imagine my unbridled delight when only ten days later a cheque for £8,300 arrived, the cost of the actual building. If only I had told them that the building was to cost £50,000, we could have built it in the Bahamas . . .

Now that we had the money we were able to get cracking with the works. It was going to be very expensive to get contractors in, so I rang the Probation Office in Colchester and asked for a group of workers from the Young Offenders Scheme. This scheme involves community service to be done by first-time law breakers. They are given a certain number of hours' work helping other people as a way of compensating for their offences, which cover a vast range from burglary to taking and driving away cars. The lads were duly organised and I then had to find a surveyor to advise on the laying out of the foundations. At that time, Mick Gillman, a local civil engineer, happened to come into school to avail himself of the cheap photocopying service we had recently offered to help offset our own copying costs. He was daft enough to tell me what his job was and from there on he was trapped in the snare. With the offer of free photocopying for life, he parted with four hundred pounds' worth of his skills and the foundations were soon laid.

The young offenders then swung into action. One of them, at least seven feet ten inches tall, was given instant promotion to foreman—you don't mess around with a human J.C.B. All the lads proved to be remarkably keen. Who wouldn't be? They had escaped prison by the skin of their teeth and were now able to vent their energies on digging and concreting and, at the same time, were being plied with coffee galore by my lovely staff. What more could a man want? On top of all this, many of them were astonished to see the problems the children had and soon stopped complaining about their own lot in life.

Once the groundworks were completed, it was only a small task for the manufacturers to deliver the building on three lorries and get it heaved into place. I then went in at 5.00 a.m. for a week and saw to the painting side of things. With a lot of help from many very generous people, we had all the equipment we thought we needed and the two staff I had chosen from the school to run the nursery left their posts in school and began the job of organising the venture. They were quite panicky about what they were actually expected to do in there, but I could not really tell them. None of us had ever worked with the extremely young autistic child, but I told them just to get stuck in and see how it went. 'Like we always do in main school when we get a new child,' said one. 'Indeed,' I replied. 'But,' said her colleague, 'these are only babies.' To set their minds at rest, I wrote the motto at the front of this book and had a wall plaque made of it for the nursery wall.

The first two children into the nursery, in June 1983, were three years old and two and a half. The three-year-old was a beautiful little girl called Laura and the other child was Daniel. Laura needs a section on her own because she is one of our great successes so far. Daniel was an extremely tiny little boy who had the most appalling temper, which he was quite happy to demonstrate at the drop of a hat. Whenever he was thwarted in any way at all, out came the temper. Of course, all children show temper tantrums quite frequently, but at the age of two and a half, rising three, most children have some language, quite a lot of comprehension and certainly a good idea of following basic commands. All Daniel wanted to do was play with the same toy all day long, and he refused to walk, choosing instead to shuffle everywhere on his knees. He had no language and no apparent understanding of normal channels of communication. There was also no sign whatsoever of any attempt to start toilet-training. The normal display of Daniel's temper came in the form of breath-holding. He would sink to the floor, wherever he was, totally oblivious of any possible dangerous objects, and hold his breath until he went purple in the face. His parents had always rushed to his aid whenever he performed like this and they used to kiss and cuddle him. This was hardly surprising because it was very distressing to watch and the family were prepared to stop it at all costs. However, I pointed out to them that what they were doing was in fact reinforcing his unacceptable behaviour by giving him a very pleasant response when he only gave them something nasty. The more they kissed and cuddled him for his misdemeanours, the more he would do the breath-holding, and the longer it went on the more difficult it would be to stop, with more chance of it becoming a very hard-to-break habit.

When I spoke to his parents about it I assured them that I was certainly not trying to criticise them and that, indeed, in their shoes, I would have followed suit, but that the only way Daniel would ever realise the error of his ways was to have it pointed out to him in no uncertain terms that what he was doing was totally unacceptable. His mother admitted that she worried herself sick about him when he began to go purple, but also agreed that he never actually seemed to come to grief during these episodes. She also asked why she had never before been told that she might be tackling it all wrongly, by the legions of doctors who had seen him in the past, instead of being told that he would outgrow it. I assured her that from the outbursts that we had seen, even the worst ones when he actually passed out, he always began to breathe again as his body took over. After each turn he never seemed to be any worse off. The only damage that was occurring seemed to me to be that caused to the family structure, as Daniel's manipulation of the family reached greater pitch. At less than three years old he had the whole family in the palm of his hand.

Following agreement with his family that we had to get him sorted out, we devised a programme of instant response. We selected his toileting as a base to work from because this was very frequently the trigger for his temper. We had often heard of all sorts of aids for toileting, both electrical and mechanical, which could be used to let a child know that he had performed successfully in the toilet or the potty. I feel that the problem with these is that they are all expensive and unnecessary. Instead I suggested that a sheet of clear plastic would catch Daniel's water if he did a wee in the toilet; he would be able to see it and be praised. This was the first step in his programme and it worked a treat, with precious little expense. As soon as Daniel was taken to the toilet as part of a regular toileting programme he would do one of two things. He would either 'perform' as requested, although this was rare, or, more usually, he would hold his breath. If he did so now he was at all times to be totally ignored until he had finished and then he was to be very severely reprimanded for doing what he had done. On the other hand, if he did perform, he was shown the results of his efforts on the plastic, given a Smartie and more kisses, cuddles, praise and contact than he ever thought possible. The fond hope was that he would realise the very exaggerated difference between the two approaches and gradually choose the right one.

As I wrote in Chapter Five, there is often an increase in undesirable behaviour until the child begins to realise the plan. In Daniel's case this is exactly how things went. The breath-holding increased dramatically and he cried and screamed and yelled far more than ever before. His mother reported the same thing, but said she was quite willing to continue if we were. At the end of the first week we were definitely able to see a reduction in the problem and this was not just wishful thinking. As usual, we had faithfully and slavishly recorded everything as carefully as possible and, looking at the records, we were able to see a fifty per cent decrease in breath-holding and a significant increase in the toileting success rate, coupled with an upsurge in the sales graphs at the Smartie factory! As the weeks passed the breath-holding was almost totally eliminated at home and at school, although the little charmer still keeps it as a weapon when he is really peeved about something.

Daniel's language is still very limited and he tends to babble baby-fashion. He can, however, make his needs known and is frequently heard actually to ask for the toilet. He is given regular language teaching, such as object recognition and simple instructions. Over the months he has grasped the ability to carry more than one instruction at once, such as 'go to the kitchen and find a cup'. The first time he managed this he did exactly that. A normal child would have worked out for himself that the given instructions inferred a third unspoken one—that is, 'Bring it back to me.' Because these children are so very limited in their verbal skills and therefore their reasoning ability, Daniel did not return. His teacher went to find him and there he was, in the kitchen, holding a cup. He had done exactly what he was asked to do and no more. The next step will be to teach in the third instruction and then, when he is felt to be ready, the third instruction will be dropped and we will hope that he infers it and does it without help. As ever, all this will be done very slowly, because success is vital in each step before you move on to the next.

During 1984 we took three new children into the nursery unit. Philip, Thomas and Christopher all arrived at once but three days after them, most unfortunately, so did two of HM Inspectors from the Department of Education and Science, because, although we are an independent school, we are still monitored by the State. The three new children were very difficult and the HMI visit was chaotic. They were both impressed, but perhaps that was because they thought we looked organised and also because we possibly appeared to know a lot more about these children than they did.

Philip arrived with no language but a scream. He was three years old and totally terrified of the world around him. The taxi driver reported that he had screamed non-stop all the way from home twelve miles away, and it was obvious that he had no intention whatsoever of stopping. His parents reported that he understood nothing and that he never came near them voluntarily. When he was approached he screamed even more. It appeared that his sole pleasure in life was food, which he devoured with gusto. We noted on preliminary visits to the home, and visits by the parents to school, that the parents rushed around trying to pacify him as soon as he screamed and, when I pointed out to them that they might just be reinforcing the bad habit, they were amazed. His mother's view was that he obviously cried for something and that, because he could not talk, it was up to them as parents to try to determine his needs. I could see their reasoning and, if I had been as emotionally involved as they were, I would have done the same; but as professionals, I pointed out, we have the time, the physical energy and the ability to be detached enough to assess a situation from the sidelines, and to spot other reasons for and patterns in behaviour.

Once I had got this point over to Philip's parents, we were able to start work on the child. The first task was to try to find a way to reduce the screams. There would be little point in trying to teach such a child to hang his coat up or to sit down, if he persisted in screaming his head off. The first thing we really spotted was that Philip's noise increased proportionally with the proximity of people and diminished as they backed off. This gave several pointers. Here was a child who had been deemed to be without communication and yet here he was, communicating beautifully that he wished to be alone and that the world was a frightening enough place without people sticking their noses into his life. The noise continued most of the time, so we decided to isolate him to see if that would stop him long enough to give us a chance to intervene briefly before he got the chance to start again. The first time he was evicted from the room it worked. 'A blessed miracle,' we said. I went to investigate. 'Wrong,' I said. He had been put in the only place available, which was the small entrance porch to the unit. One door led back into the main room where all the staff and children were. The other led to the bathroom/toilet/shower area and that is where I found him, paddling in the shower, giggling happily to himself. So in one fell swoop we had rewarded him for screaming, but at least we had a pointer to something he enjoyed and which we could possibly use for a reward system once we got to know him better.

The next move was obvious. We had to find a more suitable spot to isolate him. After a quick call to the Chairman of the governors to get permission, and another to the accountant to see if we could afford it, I was able to ring the manufacturers of the building to order a 'lock on' extension, which they had in stock. It was delivered two days later and was in use immediately. It consisted simply of a two by two-and-a-half metre room, with high windows and no possible distractions. Philip's next isolation session was in this room and failed totally to silence him. After the first time in there—not all day long, I hasten to add—we thought that more was needed. So the principle was reversed. He would not be isolated at all but forced to accept a person with him. The staff member went into the room with him as soon as he kicked up his usual din, sat on the floor with him and wrapped herself round his body. Head pressed tightly against his so that she could not be butted, chest as protected as possible from flying elbows, legs wrapped round him tightly to avoid flying feet. The first time it happened he went absolutely wild and fought for over one and a half hours. Horrendous though it may have been, cruel though it may have appeared to a stranger, we felt it had to be done. At the age of three he was containable, but we have learnt from bitter experience that these children do not lose phases once they begin, rather they tend to persevere with the same patterns, and what is hopefully manageable in a small child soon becomes impossible with a teenager.

Eventually, over a couple of weeks, Philip began to see that he was wasting his time in getting upset when these dreadful people came near him. They quite clearly were determined to win, and although he was of similar mind, they were bigger than he was and there were more of them. As the light dawned on him he began to accept our closeness and, each time he regressed and started to squawk again, he got the same treatment. Like so many children in our care, he seems to have a good memory and regression needs only very little correction.

Although three years seems a long time, we have found that progress is exceptionally slow in all these children. In the nursery the emphasis is on the groundings. We try to teach self-care, dressing and washing skills and the absolute basics of language. Tremendous importance is placed on trying to teach the child to comply with simple instructions, such as coming to the teacher on command, sitting down when told and generally conforming to the necessary routine of a school, and hopefully the child is then able to do the same at home. One way to ensure that this progress has the best chance of being maintained is to persuade the parents that their approach must be as consistent as possible with ours, and usually they do their utmost to fall in line. It also stands to reason that if the parents have found their own technique that really works, then we go along with them. In this way the communication goes both ways and if we are *ad unum* with the family, there is more chance of everyone benefiting.

In Philip's short time in the nursery he has learnt to dress himself with help, he can feed himself independently with a fork, is struggling to master a knife and is able to carry out simple commands such as, 'Put the tissue in the bin' or 'Put this book on the table'. He has learnt a couple of Makaton signs, such as 'drink' and 'more', and has mastered one word, 'ta'. A small start, but a start nevertheless. He now enjoys activities such as colour work, water play and basic sorting and matching; his concentration is very limited but he does not get angry and upset when made to persevere. At one time he was terrified of the pool and used to go mad when he was taken in there, but now he splashes around with total confidence and drinks at least ten gallons a session. He tends to whine when he has to come out. Philip's greatest plus now is that he actually enjoys physical contact and in fact loves romping on the floor. He very often instigates fun and games and when he is tickled he giggles with a very deep belly laugh, which is music to the ears, especially when compared to the thunder of his screams only two years ago.

Thomas was a totally different kettle of fish. He was unusual in that he had plenty to say for himself, or so it at first appeared. Everyone had told us about his fluent language, but when it was recorded and analysed it was mostly jargon, parroting things he had heard in his four short years. He looked intently at people when they were talking to him, again unusual in a group of children who are said to give no eye contact. He would sit patiently listening as you said something relatively simple like, 'Put the bag on the table'. Then he would proceed to take the bag and hold it until a member of staff actually physically held his hand and showed him how to complete the task. He was extremely anxious and was always asking, 'When Tom's taxi?' or 'Mummy there?' Almost everything he said was in a sort of shorthand and always restricted to concrete things. Conceptual language was totally absent, so words like 'why' and 'if' were meaningless. The best word I could find to describe this little lad was 'fragmented'. Whereas many of the other children who come to us seem to have failed to 'start' in life, in that they are so disturbed that nothing of value seems to go in, Thomas had started but had got everything mixed up and back to front. This was probably a bigger problem, because having grasped a few basics, he had to go back to square one to unlearn many things.

A very big problem for his family was that his parents had been told so often by well-meaning relatives and friends—and, sad to say, by psychologists and doctors—that Thomas was quite normal and 'just a bit behind', that they had started to believe it themselves, in spite of the fact that they could see him lagging further and further behind and especially when they saw the huge strides being made by his younger brother. It involved a tremendous amount of willpower and soul-searching to enable them to accept that his apparent normality was only a veneer, masking his very severe problems. I used a few examples to show them what I was driving at. One morning I went into the nursery and said, 'Hello, Thomas, and what are you doing this morning?' 'Me sit on chair,' was the response. Another day he was asked, 'What is this pencil for?' to which he replied, 'Not four, two.'

Thomas had a 'thing' about diggers and must have thought he was in paradise when a construction site began work at the back of the school. He could see the diggers at work from the nursery windows and this was a perfect excuse for him to reduce his already very short concentration span. We were gradually able to limit this obsession by constantly telling him that he could see the diggers if he did the task in hand first. The language and the setting of the activity had to be very carefully organised. It was important to sit him so that he actually had to turn round to see the diggers, so that it would be possible to pre-empt him. It was also important to structure the language so that he could have a chance of understanding the deal. It would have been pointless to say, 'As soon as you've done this you can go and see the diggers.' A child with normally developing language would have been able to filter out the necessary words, 'this' and 'diggers'; he would have heard them in sequence and retained that sequence, knowing instantly that the second only came as a consequence of the first. Perhaps it is a miracle in itself that most children can in fact sort out all this information going into their brains and respond accordingly.

In Thomas's case it was a question of saying, 'Do this', and physically stopping him from turning round; then the instant he completed the task he was told, 'Diggers now' and allowed to turn round. By doing it this way there was also a better chance that he would not automatically expect to be allowed to see the diggers as soon as he had done his work and that he would then accept a sweet or a kiss and cuddle as a reward for his efforts; later he might just accept praise for doing it, which is a much more normal way of doing things. It also made life easier for all concerned, because the diggers would not be there forever. If the reward had been expected every single time, he might only have done a task as a way of seeing the diggers and then would have been mortified when they left for good. As it turned out, he had been led to other things when the famous diggers left and he never even realised that they had gone. It was only when the swimming pool was dug out that he revived his interest in diggers, but by then it was no longer an obsession and he was genuinely interested. His language had improved and developed enough for him to talk sensibly, although still in shorthand, and he finished up in the cab with the driver, operating the grab arm while I took a photo of him. That photo remains his prize possession, although he only rarely talks about diggers.

Since Thomas joined the nursery he has made great strides, but he has a long way to go. He began to put tremendous pressure on his family and then he began to react to the strain and tension. His sleeping patterns disintegrated and he began to be very defiant. His mother felt that it all started because he needed so much attention and his three brothers were losing out on the attention they also needed. His father had a demanding job and could not give his wife the support she wanted. Once this vicious circle was created there seemed to be only one way to break it and that was for the child to be away from home for a large part of the week. This would mean that his brothers would get all the attention they needed, his parents would have the pressure lifted off them and Thomas himself would be able to relax. If he could relax he could learn more, and the whole scene could be turned into an 'unvicious circle'. So it was that Thomas changed status from day-child to boarder, and, after a few upset nights when he asked for his mother, he settled in and now accepts his new lifestyle. It then came out that his mother had spent a few evenings weeping to herself as well, but she knew that it was for her child's sake and that of her whole family, and she and her husband soon accepted the situation. The joy in the family is now scarcely contained when Thomas goes home.

When Daniel moved into main school in 1985, his place was taken by a human dynamo called Cavan. He is an incredibly good-looking lad, aged nearly four when he arrived. He was not so much disturbed as totally out of control. At that age he had never been to school before and had ruled the roost at home. He came into the nursery but was staying in school as a boarder. This in itself created a problem because it meant that he had to get used to the actual nursery staff who would be in charge of him: all the nursery children have had to do this, but they go home each night to the regime they already know. Cavan had to get to know the system in school as well, which meant learning the two-shift systems which we use. This involved one shift of early care staff every morning one week and a different group of late staff in the evening, and then on top of all that he had to get to know the night staff. It was not the best situation for him to be in, but it was the best we had to offer. The Local Authority and his parents were keen on a boarding placement and we only had a boarding place for a child who could go in the nursery rather than into a class in the main school. One thing that the placement did achieve was to underline the very important need to hold regular case meetings between all staff, so that they all knew exactly what was expected of them and what was being done with each child—especially Cavan, who spends his days in the nursery, away from the staff in the main school.

Cavan, as I mentioned, was a dynamo, a human whirlwind who found it totally impossible to keep still for more than seconds at a time. He had been described as hyperactive, which is a well-worked statement often used to disguise a more suitable comment, such as 'badly handled and downright naughty', but he was a classic example of the hyperactive syndrome. In spite of all his parents' efforts he was totally out of their control. He was built like a tank and had destroyed the home, both physically and emotionally. He was constantly on the go, damaging things, tearing anything that was tearable and obsessed with ripping paper of any sort, especially books. He refused to eat properly and gave vent to his temper as soon as he was frustrated in his activities by going absolutely crazy. In the early days it took three full-grown adults to hold him down when he went over the top, to prevent him demolishing everything in sight. He had quite a few words but no spontaneous language, was not toilet trained and refused or was unable to sleep for more than an hour at a time. It seemed impossible to get him into any sort of routine.

Quite often, when a new child comes on the scene, some of his problems are more pressing than others and we work on the worst one first. In Cavan's case we could not even begin to guess where to start, so we took the total blitz approach. This involved a 'simultaneous all fronts attack' on everything he did wrong. The emphasis in this approach was placed on the need to seek desperately for something done well or correctly, so that the positive thinking could be applied and the praise could be heaped on him. The first week passed in a welter of paper tearing, toy damaging, pants wetting and mind-bending screaming, with virtually no sleep at all. Things were so bad that our usual day and night record book was not big enough to hold all the details about Cavan's days and nights and we had to have a separate book just for him. For some reason he seemed to respond slightly better to me as the only man in the place, but even so he was very awkward for me as well.

However, as the days went by, we began to see subtle changes in his behaviour. Every single time he did something wrong he was roared at and physically forced to stop. If he stopped he was praised. Whenever he leaped out of bed a member of staff who was hiding at the side of the bed in the dark would jump up and roar at him to get back into bed. If he got back in he was praised. Although this method would have put the fear of the Lord into most children, Cavan was undeterred for three months and was up and down from his bed at least thirty times in as many minutes until he settled. At last he began to stay in bed until the small hours of the morning and then the night staff had the same rigmarole, but one night, as if by a miracle, the little tyke slept all night. The joy of this success resounded round the school and if it had not been for our extremely good programme of dental hygiene, his teeth would have parted company with his gums because of all the sweets he got that morning.

The paper ripping has gone, he is now prepared to sit for long periods doing classroom activities and he sleeps virtually every night through. He eats well most days and continues to be better when I am around and better when he is in the nursery than in school in the mornings and evenings. We eventually decided to capitulate on that one, because he is still very acceptable to one and all, including his parents, and we have said that, in the final analysis, the difference between the two levels of behaviour is just Cavan being Cavan. I am well convinced of the value in some cases of the total blitz approach. If we had tackled Cavan's problems one at a time we would have been years getting him anywhere near acceptable. He now has a few meaningful words, most notably 'toilet' and 'biscuit', and the fond hope is that as the months and years go by he will acquire more words and be able to express himself more easily, and that he will then settle down and progress even further.

When Christopher came to the nursery in 1984 he had virtually no communication, apart from being able to tell people to go away by pushing them off. He was toilet-trained, which was a miracle wrought by his parents and a blessing for us. He was reported to be a dreadful sleeper, or an expert at not sleeping. He insisted on sleeping on the landing, wrapped up in his quilt, and waking every few minutes, after which he screamed the place down. He refused to eat properly and gave his parents hell at mealtimes. He had a habit which seemed trivial in itself but which, on top of everything else, drove his parents to distraction. He refused to keep his shoes on at all, wherever he was, which was obviously infuriating for them, especially if they were out in public.

The shoe phobia was the first to be worked on in the nursery because it also hindered our staff if the children were out on a walk. It turned out to be remarkably simple to achieve. Every time a shoe came off it was jammed back on extremely quickly and Chris was told off very forcefully indeed; within a very short time he stopped his antics. If he kept his shoe on for the whole period of the outing he was praised for doing so. His parents reported that he was still doing it at home and that they were having no success, so the nursery staff did their angels of mercy act by arranging a home visit. They had to go nearly forty miles each way, and that's a killer after an eight-hour day, but they went because they accept it as a necessary part of the job. Once there, they were able to see that Chris's parents were being far too gentle on him over the shoe business, so they asked permission to intervene. It was granted immediately and the next time the shoe shot off, it shot back on again as the nursery boss lady hollered at him. It stayed on for the rest of the visit. His parents were staggered at how firm they needed to be and at just how soft they had been before. They continued this regime for two more weeks and the problem disappeared.

The next time a home visit was arranged it was to teach the parents how to cope with his eating. Chris was always very hard to feed. He had, for a long time, only wanted to eat sloppy food and was obsessional about having the same dish all the time. Attempts to remove the dish caused mind-blowing screams. The staff decided that he would have to be made to eat, which involved pushing a spoonful of food into his mouth and clamping his mouth closed until he swallowed. This was repeated with every spoonful until the meal was finished. The portion was only very small, but he got there and he was lavishly praised with lots of attention, kisses and cuddles. There was also a battle about fresh fruit which his mother reported he had always totally rejected. Unfortunately Christopher's very restricted diet and objection to fresh fruit and other roughage caused him to have severe constipation, which in turn led to more bad temper, less co-operation and less desire to have anything to do with other people. The home visit clinched it. The parents had already seen the level of firmness required with the shoe trouble and were taught to apply it to the food. Within a week Christopher, at the age of four, had lost this very big battle in his war against the world.

In the last two years we have had more and more positive comments at home about how much Christopher wants to be part of the family. He has started using quite a lot of real language, although considerable time has to be spent trying to improve his articulation. Because of this improvement we were very surprised to read in his report book in the early summer of 1986 that he had suddenly regressed and was becoming very difficult again at home, although he seemed delighted to come to school. We were so worried that the girl who runs the nursery suggested that we invite the parents to school.

Christopher's mother and father observed him through the two-way mirror and felt even worse because the staff were coping with him so well, while they seemed failures. They were also shattered to see the way he was relating to and co-operating with the staff, because he was giving nothing at home. A long chat in the office established that they had unwittingly switched off from their son and were a lot more attentive to their younger daughter than to Christopher. They felt that this had happened because he does like to spend time on his own. I suggested that perhaps he was jealous of his sister and, because he did not have the language skills to express his frustration, he had chosen to be difficult again. His mother began to cry because she felt, in her words, a failure. Once the tears dried up we were able to tell her that if she were a failure her child would not still be at home, and that all she had to do was flood him with attention. This he got and came round within a week.

Jeanette was the latest addition to our 'littlies' group at Easter 1986. At the age of four, she still had very severe problems, but has improved a little in the last few months. She has the most appalling temper, and when she starts she really lets fly. Her arrival on the first day was heralded by the sound of a banshee wailing as she walked, or rather was half-carried from the taxi. She had bitten the escort, who was in need of a cup of tea before she could compose herself sufficiently to return to base. Jeannette's parents had fallen into the common trap of doing anything to keep the peace, which so many other parents have done so unwittingly. They start by giving in to the child, thinking that this is just a phase that he or she is entering and will pull out of, but it is often too late when it is pointed out that it is not a phase to be outgrown but a phase that the child has to be dragged out of.

Every single morning, as Jeanette arrived, I flicked on the intercom from the office to the nursery to hear the screeching yells from this tiny little girl. I switched off equally rapidly and uttered a silent prayer for the sanity of the girls who had to endure this, sometimes for the entire day. However, they soon found that she was starting to respond to being put into the time-out room and her screams were starting to diminish quite quickly as soon as she was away from her audience. The minute the staff went near her she started again, but gradually she calmed down enough for a member of staff to praise her for stopping the row. I shall never forget the morning when the girl in charge of the nursery buzzed me on the intercom and said, 'Can you get over here quickly?' I shot over, expecting a disaster, but when I got there she said, 'Listen.' 'I can't hear anything,' I said, mystified. 'No, neither can we,' was the answer, 'and Jeanette's here, she's in the toilet.' It was the first time in three months that she had come to school without screaming. The pleasure was only surpassed by another incident the next morning. One of the nursery staff, convinced that Jeanette did not like her, rushed around school yelling to all and sundry that Jeanette had given her a cuddle. We were all very chuffed indeed, but an outsider would have wondered what all the fuss was about.

The nursery staff spend a lot of their free time visiting the children's homes. They usually go in the holidays or just before the holidays, so that they can have direct contact with the parents apart from the weekly record book. In this way they can speak freely to staff about any new or recurring problems, and in many cases the staff can see what actually goes on in the home, and can study the child/parent interaction. Nine times out of ten the parents can be seen to be trying to do the same as us, but on home visits the staff occasionally see things happening that they would not allow in school, although the parents seem to be able to tolerate them. We accept that these parents have been to hell and back as they have tried to cope with their feelings and their problems, so now, if they are able to cope with the child and are still able to live with him happily, then all I can say is good luck to them. They deserve to have it easier than in the past.

When new children come to the nursery I always tell the parents that if they cannot get involved with our approach and sort out their child's problems while he is still very small, then their beautiful three-year-old will soon grow into a not-so-beautiful thirteen-year-old, and then into an adult who could prove to be unmanageable. If they then try to mould him into more acceptable ways, it could be far too late and crucifyingly difficult, and could result in the total breakdown of the whole family structure. This sort of advice to parents usually seems to have a profound effect. I call it the 'putting the fear of God in them' technique. It is so much easier to manipulate a three-year-old because he is not big enough to throw his weight around, nor has he had enough time to become too deeply entrenched in his dreadful ways. Once I can make parents realise that their child will not simply outgrow this devastating handicap without help, the job becomes much easier. I also point out just how lucky they are that the nursery was available for their children, when compared to many parents who, only a few years ago, had to wait so long. I am sure that the parents really do appreciate these facts. The nursery has been able to relieve the pressures on the children and on the families as early as possible, and together we have begun to work on their bizarre and unacceptable lifestyles, so as to give the whole family a chance of some level of normality. This was the whole object of the exercise when we set up the nursery. It appears to have worked.

9
OUR SUCCESSES

By way of sharp contrast to the sad stories of Matthew and J.C. who were both taken away, of Annabel and of the three children I have had to exclude as unmanageable, here are the tales of a few successes.

When David first came to school in 1983 he was eleven years old and two stone below normal body weight. I first saw him and his parents at the school he was attending in London. He was a bag of nerves, given to severe head-banging and rocking. The school's answer to this self-aggression had been to get a soft armchair for him, and every time he banged his head he was made to sit in this lovely soft chair, where he was left to carry on. His class teacher had twelve children altogether and one assistant, so it was hardly surprising that she had resorted to this method so that she could attend to the rest of the class. She simply had no time to think about any sort of behaviour modification programme for David with such a large group to help. The first thing David's parents said was, 'Please don't tell us that David's state is our fault.' When I said that anyone who had said that to them was an idiot, they were staggered. This was, they said, the first time they had not been told that they were responsible.

When I asked David's teacher if she minded my intervening in his head-banging, she told me to feel free. I approached him from behind as he blithely continued to bash his head against the delightfully soft chair and then I leaped out and literally screamed at him to stop. He almost literally jumped out of his skin. He did not bang his head for the rest of the session and I praised him liberally. His teacher looked at me as if I was a miracle worker, but I simply pointed out that the soft chair was only serving as a reward for his horrible behaviour. His parents were in the room at the time and I told them that when he came to us he would get this treatment every time, if we felt it would stop his head-banging. His father said words to the effect that he did not care what we did, so long as he got his son back. His mother was almost in a state of nervous exhaustion and felt that whatever we did could not possibly make things any worse than they were at present.

So David came to school, arriving after a very fraught journey of some fifty miles from his home in London. He walked into his new classroom with one of the staff and smashed his head through a panelled wall. His teacher went mad at him, roaring, ranting and raving at him as if to make him think he was about to meet his maker. What he did not know was that he had been set up. I had told all the staff what to expect from him and had described his antics and shown them on the video I had taken. I always film a new child when I go to see him so that the staff have some idea of what he may be like. His teacher had seen my reaction to his tricks and was totally prepared to do the same. She never went within ten feet of him, but his feet left the ground as he felt the lash of her tongue. He sat down in absolute shock and, as his bottom touched the chair, he was praised to the eyeballs and has never banged his head again.

David had some language when he came to us, but the vast majority of it was parroted. Whenever anyone spoke to him he repeated the last couple of words of their sentence. If you said to him, 'Home in a taxi or walk?' he would say, 'Walk', and if you reversed it he would then say, 'Taxi'. This was the general rule with David, he did that last word repetition almost every time he was spoken to. It proved valuable one day at the breakfast table. I had introduced brown bread as part of the children's junk-free diet and David was objecting quite strongly because he loved white bread and also, I reckoned, because this tiny change in his routine had upset him. I used his last word-repeating trick to brilliant effect by asking him, 'What colour is this bread, brown or white?' 'White,' he said. 'Well, be quiet and eat it,' I said. 'All right,' he said and scoffed it without further ado. Then he asked for more white bread and took the next slice of brown. After that he did not complain again. Fortunately for us he did not know his colours at the time.

David's parents reported to us that their son always seemed happy to get in the taxi on Monday mornings to go to school, which pleased them because they did not like the idea of his going off on a long journey if he was going to be upset, but the trouble came when he cried all the way home on a Friday. We noticed that he was getting more uptight as the week progressed and on Fridays he was thoroughly miserable. We decided that this was happening because he knew that the situation was fraught at home. He tried to rule the roost there and his parents were sinking under the onslaught. There was anger and upset, frustration and resentment in the home and David's parents would now be the first to admit that they had been very close to giving up on him. Luckily David was one of the quickest 'responders' we have had in the place. He soon calmed down a great deal and he seemed happy both to be in school and to go home. He gained enough weight to make sure he would not win the 'Scarecrow of the Year' show and seemed generally content.

Then we saw a pattern change. He began to get distressed on leaving home for school and the driver reported that he was weeping all the way. As the week passed he settled down, and we just assumed that he had got used to the school routine again, but after a few weeks of this we found that there was more to it. Although David did not know the days of the week, he had got so used to the system and the order of activities that, like any normal child, he was able to anticipate the passage of days and we realised that he was actually looking forward to the weekends because he really wanted to see his parents and to be with them. This was exactly as it should be and we were all pleased.

David still had some very irritating habits at home and he still annoyed his parents a great deal, even though they could manage him most of the time. One of his mannerisms, harmless in itself, was to twist his head, almost like a spastic child, and this, to quote his father, 'Gets right up my nose'. His teacher offered to spend the weekend in the home and quite happily volunteered to go to London. The parents put David in her capable hands for the whole weekend while they watched, listened and learned. As soon as he did his head-twisting routine she just roared at him to stop. He did. His parents soon began to realise just how firm they had not been and just how hard they had to be. The next weekend his father's 'phone conversation with me went something like this:

'Ian, I've stopped the neck-twisting at last.'

'Great, how did you do it?'

'I threatened to pull his bloody head off and he's not done it since Friday night. Mind you, I did praise him for not doing it again, just like you told us.'

Negative motivation, one might argue, but in effect, what David's father was telling us was that he had at last got the measure of his son, after twelve long years.

David is the master of the art of the use of the minor senses. He loves to tap and twiddle with objects and sniffs and licks all manner of things. He is very adept at picking up vibrations from people. When he first came to us he had a thing about people's foreheads. He would approach a person from behind and run the tip of his middle finger across his or her brow, emitting a long 'Eeeeeeee' sound as he did so. The trouble was that, as he did it from the rear, he could do it without any eye contact and we felt that this was not acceptable because he seemed to be using people to suit his own ends; we wanted him to realise that people were an important part of his life, and therefore he had to communicate with them in a normal fashion. It was only a small step for us to refuse to allow him to touch anyone from the rear. If he wanted to stroke someone's head it had to be face to face or not at all. It took only a short time for David to accept this new change and eye contact increased dramatically. The desire to touch our heads diminished of its own accord, although strangers still get the treatment. If we get the chance to forewarn them it is not too bad, but if David gets in first they are usually in for a shock.

Although most of David's language remains on the parroted level and he still has the utmost trouble with his pronouns—like saying, 'What's this?' when a visitor arrives, instead of 'Who's this?'—he sometimes comes out with a statement that is grammatically correct and seems to be appropriate. One day, when I was in his classroom, he suddenly said to me, 'I wanna see you in the office!' I followed him dutifully to my office where he told me to sit down. This I did and then waited with bated breath. David grabbed hold of an empty coffee cup and said, 'I fink I'll wash this.' He took the cup to the kitchen, washed it, dried it, put it away and went back to his classroom, so I still await his pronouncement.

One afternoon he was cooking in the kitchen, baking a cake. He had, under close supervision, succeeded in producing a sponge cake which had to be cut in half and filled. The two halves were side by side awaiting the filling and the girl who specialises in cookery gave him a bowl of cream and a jar of jam. She helped him to put the jam on one side and then told him to put the cream on the jam. David heard the words 'cream' and 'jam' and reversed them in his own inimitable fashion, so that, hearing the word 'jam' last, he assumed he had to put the jam on the cream. Without further ado he scraped the jam off the cake and slopped it into the cream bowl. It was suggested by the member of staff that he stop and think (the suggestion did sound very much like the word 'stop' shouted very loudly) and David froze. 'Now then,

David,' she said, 'put the cream on the jam.' She guided his hands to help him put a further layer of jam on and then mimicked the movement from cream bowl to cake, forgetting to indicate the need to use a spoon. 'Oh yeah,' said David, plunged his hands into the cream bowl and flicked the mixture of cream and jam vaguely in the direction of the cake, liberally spattering the stuff all over the table, the staff and himself. At this juncture I happened to be passing through and asked him what he was doing. He uttered the time-honoured phrase, 'Bit of a bleedin' mess innit?' His parents were delighted and his father promised to watch his language.

* * *

Alexander first came to school when he was nine. He was an extremely anxious child and this anxiety had rubbed off on to his family, so that the whole situation was fraught. He was in the habit of asking to see the moon and the stars. This had started as an apparently harmless desire to see them as he went to bed, but before long his parents found that he was asking later and later, and he then took to asking them for the moon and the stars after they had gone to bed. The final straw came when he asked them at three o'clock in the morning, which was not the most appropriate time of day to make such a request. This, coupled with all his anxiety and defiance, which made him very hard to live with, forced his parents to ask their Education Authority for a place at Doucecroft. He had been to see many doctors who had all pronounced him autistic, but no suggestion had ever been made for him to attend a school for autistic children. Another example of creative accountancy, I feel, because that particular Authority did not have a school and probably could not afford to set one up. Alexander was in fact referred to us by a paediatrician who was on our Board of Governors at the time, and without this doctor he might have floundered.

At bedtime on his first night, Alexander was found by the night staff, staring out of the bedroom window. He was asked what he wanted and replied that he was looking for the moon and the stars. A loud voice, somewhat similar to that of an RSM, was sufficient to suggest to him that it might be a good idea if he were to get himself into bed. Not many children had cleared ten feet in one bound but Alexander certainly did that night. It only needed two more consecutive nights totally to eliminate this problem, although it persisted for some time at home until his parents were able to learn the same technique. Like David, Alexander was very quick to catch on and I cannot remember ever having to set up any specific programmes to deal with his behaviour patterns, apart from the one we needed to help overcome his pathological fear of dogs. He had once been nipped on his cheek by a family puppy and after that he was mortally afraid of all dogs. The programme simply involved desensitisation, which means working through a series of stages beginning with pictures and working back to the real thing. It took a long time but he is now reasonably calm when he sees a dog.

During the dog programme, Alexander found the need to talk about dogs a great deal and took to asking every single visitor the following three questions: 'What is your name?' 'Where do you come from?' and 'Have you got a dog?' One day when we had had several visitors, the conversation was beginning to wear a bit thin, so I warned the next visitor and told Alexander that he was not to ask about dogs. Having established the next person's name and provenance he then stopped, twisted his face into a very deep thinking pose and said, 'Have you got any pets?' His aside to me was, 'I didn't ask about dogs, Ian.' This was the first time that Alexander had shown any real insight into the use of language and, from that day on, it seemed that a tap had been opened. He became more and more proficient, but some of the more complex parts of language continued to evade him. For example, when he had an ingrowing toenail seen to, he failed totally to understand the instructions the doctor gave him for after care. I went through it with him but he only grasped the idea when I gave him a full demonstration, actually using a bowl with salt and water to demonstrate a foot bath. It took a long time to sink in and then he said, 'But that's not a bath, Ian, it's a washing-up bowl!'

Over the years Alexander has become our most reliable child. He enjoys simple reading and writing exercises, he does pottery and derives much pleasure from it. He loves swimming and tolerates horse riding. He often shows his sense of humour but never more than when another child is in trouble, which is so very typical of a teenager. Alexander is one of the few children who seems ready to work things out and to think for himself. He likes nothing more than to be left on his own in the kitchen making a cake and, if there is anything he cannot find, he looks for it first, then comes to ask. One day, when he could not find any eggs, he just helped himself to the cook's own, which she planned to take home for tea, having done her shopping at lunchtime.

* * *

If I were ever asked to name my favourite child it would have to be Laura. She is the most beautiful child I have ever set eyes on. She started in the nursery as a total parrot, given to wandering around and chuntering to herself non-stop. She churned out every word and expression that had ever entered her memory bank from outside sources; there was no eye contact whatsoever, no response to other people; she gave no affection to anyone, especially her parents, and the only thing that had any real value for her was an obsession with books. She was not interested in actually looking at the books; instead she spent all her time flicking the pages over and bending them. She used to steal her mother's cheque book so that she would have something to flick in the taxi on the way to school and, if the staff's backs were turned, she would grab hold of any book she could get her hands on, then sit quietly in a corner, looking round to see if she had been spotted.

This book thing was quite easy to control because only a few stages were needed to eliminate the problem. Step one was to put a total ban on books. Step two was to allow her to look, and only look, at books in the presence of a member of staff. Step three was to allow her to look at books alone but they were whipped away the moment she gave any indication that she planned to have a sneaky flick.

The trouble is that when you ban something which you consider to be meaningless, like flicking books, there is a tendency to consider it meaningless in normal terms, whereas the activity may not only be meaningful to the child, it could be vital. Such an activity is likely to be a source of great comfort to the child and a means of keeping his equilibrium, as necessary as a crutch to a disabled person. Unfortunately, all too often, obsessions take over and rule the child's life, blocking other development along acceptable lines. The crutch, if it is to be removed, has to be replaced with something that we consider to be more normal. This something 'more normal' has to be an activity which is considered acceptable and beneficial to the child. Most children eventually realise that they have to perform on such a level, but a sad fact of being handicapped is that, being unable to see this yourself, someone has to make you fit in, because otherwise society will finally reject you. Laura eventually got the idea and the book-flicking was replaced by a desire to sit with a member of staff, looking at books together.

One of Laura's endearing qualities was that she had a thing about bottoms. The nursery children and staff have a regular outing every week to the local Sports Centre for swimming. In the changing rooms one day she saw a rather buxom lady getting changed. This lady wore flowery pants, another of Laura's fancies. She rushed over to the lady and, having stroked her beflowered behind, thrust her nose super-close, inhaled deeply and said in a very loud, deep voice, 'Big bottom.' The lady in question did not seem to appreciate in any way, shape or form my educational theories about encouraging the use of the minor senses, especially when the perpetrator of the deed was such an incredibly normal-looking little girl. The problem was not rendered any less confusing by Daniel who, on spotting the lady's rather prominent pectoral appendages, pointed and uttered a prolonged 'Oooh!' The staff were well used to such embarrassing moments and not at all disconcerted, but the lady was, and the whole situation was not helped in the slightest by the genteel lady who runs the nursery when she issued the immortal statement, 'You need eyes in your backside with these two.'

Laura has very long blonde hair which is quite fine. After Christmas her mother was hoovering up the pine needles from the Christmas tree and Laura was lying on the floor because she liked the noise made by the vacuum. Suddenly a large chunk of hair was grabbed by the cleaner and became tangled round the rollers. For the first time in her life Laura was genuinely upset and screamed her head off. Her mother was amazed because for the first time, Laura allowed herself to be cuddled. When her father arrived home from work he was given an account of what had happened and assumed that it had taken place only a few minutes before. When he was told that in fact it had occurred some two hours before, he wondered why she was still being cuddled. Her mother's answer was that she had not been given this opportunity in all of Laura's five years and she was not going to miss out on it now.

When she first came to the nursery, Laura was a very poor eater. She used to kick up a tremendous fuss every time she was made to sit at the table, and we resorted to taking her away from the other children, so that at least they could eat in peace. We started off with a system of instant reward every time Laura ate something. As soon as she swallowed a mouthful of food she was given a Smartie, followed by the next mouthful. It used to take a long time to get her food down, except when she had her three favourites, which, in her way of talking, were 'sossinges, 'orkshire pudding and beef buggers'. The fact that she ate these without a fuss indicated that she had been allowed to have just what she wanted. Her parents admitted this, but as soon as it was pointed out, it stopped at home and she was made to eat everything. With this consistency guaranteed at home and at school, it did not take Laura long to eat properly, especially the sossinges!

Laura used to be terrified of water and would scream blue murder when she went, or rather was taken, into the swimming pool, but now she gets very cross indeed when it is time to get out. After she learned to swim her parents took her to their local beach where her mother reported that they had to stop her going out too far. She was half-way to France, said her mother, but she was able to laugh about it all, whereas not long before she had been a bundle of nerves because of the pressure she was under with her child.

Laura's non-stop chuntering has hardly ever diminished, although we have noted that she uses spontaneous language when she is particularly peeved about something. One day she was sick to death of hearing Daniel's screams, so she suddenly erupted and said, 'For Godsake stop skweeming.' Very often she hollers, 'It's not fair,' when she has to come out of the pool. This spontaneous language is still quite rare, although her comprehension has improved dramatically. Laura is guaranteed to make everyone laugh when she says things like 'bloody Thatcher', no doubt after her father watched a party political broadcast, and staff were seen biting their fists to stop themselves laughing till they cried when one day she was heard to say that the 'fkolologist' was coming to visit. One day, when Laura heard someone say that she was absolutely beautiful, she repeated the word, but it came out as 'absolutee' and now, three years on, when a member of staff agrees with a colleague she will invariably use the school catch-word, 'absolutee'. Visitors must think we are crazy.

* * *

In his parents' words, Scott was a monster who had made their lives a misery in his early years. He almost never stopped screaming and was oblivious of their very existence. We first set eyes on him at the age of five, when his prospective teacher and I went to the school in which he was placed. It was actually an 'observation unit', but eventually he would have to leave. The unit is a sort of distribution centre for children. Their needs are analysed and then recommendations are made for future placement in specialist schools if the need is considered to be there. Unfortunately, because of lack of resources, the children are often moved on to schools which cannot cater for their needs or even begin to cope with them. Scott was one of the lucky ones because he was put forward to us. He spent as much of his free time as he could hiding in corners and he was at his happiest doing nothing apart from flapping his hands and twiddling with toy car wheels. Any attempts at intervention caused horrendous screaming. We soon found that Scott used his screaming as a way of driving people away, so we resolved to stay near him. If he ran away he was followed. It took a good five months before we got through to Scott. We had a plan whereby the staff with him would hold on tight and demand that he be quiet. If he did not stop, a hand was put over his mouth until he did so, and the instant he stopped he was given a sweet. Our recording sheet showed a severe increase in screaming for five days, followed by a slight reduction, then a greater one. Finally we found Scott apparently enjoying people being around, and he began to accept kisses and cuddles very readily. The next step forward came when he began to seek out the physical attention he was beginning to get so much pleasure from.

When Makaton was introduced to Scott it was like a whole new world opening up for him. He picked up the signs very quickly and with them the beginnings of language. When he signs toast, he tries desperately hard to say the word, but only manages the initial sound of the word so far. However, we at school and his parents at home can understand him and his articulation is improving slowly. He enjoys books and is starting on the rudiments of reading. One thing that makes Scott stand out from the other children is that he seems to be very motivated to do things and seems to derive great pleasure from completing a task. The completion in itself appears to be just reward for his efforts, but 'job satisfaction' on this level for one of our children is very unusual and pleasing. If Scott is doing something and is told to stop for lunch, he gets quite cross and insists on finishing. A far cry from his first days when his only skill was screaming.

* * *

The children I have described in this chapter are successes for us because they have responded so well to our intervention in their lives. But more than that, their parents have been able to accept them for what they are and they are much loved members of their families, in spite of the fact that they remain very handicapped in relation to their peers and will continue to need care and education for years to come, perhaps for the rest of their lives. As Laura's mother once said, 'We now live each day as it comes and in between all the pain we see our daughter grow and develop and she is often a great source of joy to us.' As far as I know, that's all I want from and for my own non-handicapped child.

10
TEACHING METHODS

It is very difficult to stipulate what teaching methods should be used with any child, and particularly with children whose problems are as severe as those in my school. Therefore the following is not a categorical statement of how it should be done, although some of the ideas could be applied to all autistic children. I have explained in Chapter Five how we try to teach children to control their frustration and thus their tempers, although obviously this is not done separately from day-to-day living.

It is accepted that there is a sliding scale of severity in the disorder, as there is in most handicaps. Some schools have tended towards the less disturbed, more able autistic child, arguing that these are perhaps the children for whom more can be done. When Doucecroft opened, however, perhaps because the Local Authorities were testing us out, we were asked to take some extremely difficult and disturbed children, many of whom had been rejected by other schools as being too unmanageable. The Authorities are not quite so desperate to place the quieter, more able child in private schools if they can be coped with in State schools, which may have something to do with cost. Whatever the reasons, the majority of children put forward to me have been very 'far gone' and well-skilled in the art of family destruction. I know that there are children suffering from autism who do not have temper tantrums and who, if anything, are too quiet, but we have not had many such children put forward.

The first target, as discussed in Chapter Five, is to

eliminate explosions of temper. Without doing this I am convinced that any further steps are a total and utter waste of time. The first step after this must be to establish control over the child, to form a link which will lead to co-operation from him. This sounds easy and is anything but easy. You are faced with a child who appears to look straight through you, who does not seem to hear and who shows no willingness whatsoever to begin to co-operate.

The first stage in the operation is to put the child in a position where he cannot escape, and for this it needs the teacher to be very close to the child in a sitting position. Of course, if the child does not like people too near him you have got problems! If the child plans to run off he has to get himself into the standing position first, which gives the teacher a chance to dive in and stop him. It is important to select a simple activity so that too much is not expected of the child; then he must be made to perform a task. If he cannot do it or refuses to do it, his hands need to be guided in the movements of the task. Let us suppose that you require him to thread two beads onto a string. This is not necessarily the reason that you asked him to sit down in the first place. The ability to thread beads is not crucial to his development at this stage; what is crucial is his ability to follow a command and to co-operate actively, so the bead-threading is simply a means to an end. The activity could well be holding a pencil and drawing a line, even with your hand over his. It would be very unfair in the initial stages simply to request that the child should sit on demand and then have nothing to occupy him.

It is extremely likely that the child will try everything in his repertoire to escape the situation, particularly if this is the first concerted effort in his life to make him conform. He may revert to type and have a temper tantrum, slightly different from the usual ones which seem to have no explanation, and he could well be so used to getting out of situations with such tantrums that he fails to realise that you, as the teacher, will not tolerate such screaming and yelling. The task of the school is to break down the barriers between the child and the outside world, and this can only be achieved by a very strong determination to win. Indeed, as I have said before, one of my favourite statements is, 'Don't start a battle unless you intend to win.'

Another trick the child may resort to is to start to use every avoidance technique he has at his disposal. He may begin his strange hand movements: they can be stopped by physically holding his hands. He may refuse point blank to look at the task: this can sometimes be overcome by the teacher actually turning the child's head. If he then averts his gaze, another problem has arisen, because you cannot swivel the child's eyeballs for him. Whatever approach the child takes, the task must be completed, however upset he may become. Even if he has caused such a rumpus that the other children are becoming upset, he must still be made to conform. He may have to be removed from the scene and be isolated until he calms down, and then he must be taken back to the work and be made to continue. Each time he is removed, and this may be very frequent, he needs to be praised for calming down, because he has been ejected with the inference, 'You stay there till you're quiet'. By stopping his screaming he has done something right, which has to be recognised.

The moment the child actually achieves the desired objective the praise has to be instant. 'Good boy', said in a very casual, offhand manner, is by no means enough. After all, the teacher has had to be prepared to 'get heavy' if the child refused to participate, so she has to be equally forceful with the praise. If this pattern is followed, it can be almost guaranteed that some measure of success can be achieved.

Once the child has started to conform to the new regime, you are still only on step one. An autistic child does not easily develop the ability to generalise, because language is needed for the thought processes involved in working things out for himself. He may start by responding only to the person who manipulated him into conforming in the first place. This is useless, because if the child only responds to one person and that person is absent or leaves, he is well and truly 'snookered'. Every person working with the children has to learn how to tackle them all. Even the youngest trainee has to be taught the ropes, often with a more experienced teacher to begin with.

If you have taught a skill in the classroom, it does not follow that the child can perform the same thing elsewhere. He may learn to count blocks or counters in the classroom, but then fail to count knives and forks when you try to get him to lay the table in the dining-room. If this situation arises, it is a useless statement to say that he can count. He can only count things that you have taught him and cannot transfer the knowledge to other objects, so you have to start again. Far better, perhaps, to have taught him to count cutlery in the first place. We were able to teach one child to fasten his left shoelace over a period of two years, five minutes a day. Eventually he mastered the skill and was then asked to fasten his other shoe. He immediately blew his top and screamed for quite some time. We had chosen the left shoe simply because the majority of staff are right-handed, and so it was easier to reach his hands to guide them when sitting opposite him. It became crystal-clear that we had not taught him to fasten his shoes but to fasten his left one and to him, in his very fragmented brain, the other shoe was a totally different kettle of fish. Four months later he was able to fasten both shoes, after we had reverted to the same five minutes a day of the same patient demonstration and hand-moving technique. Three weeks later, his mother decided he looked better in slip-ons and has provided nothing else since! Wise to the possibility of regression, we have kept him in practice with a spare pair, just in case he ever gets another pair of lace-ups.

Even the most patient among us would flinch at the thought of having to do the same thing over again for another two years.

A large problem for our children is that they have difficulty in becoming aware of their own identity and even of their own existence. It is important to teach a child that he exists in relation to others, but first he needs to learn about himself. We use individual photographs of the child to get over to him what he looks like, where his different body parts are and how he is 'assembled'. Mirrors are also used a great deal for the same reason. Each day the photographs are put out in each child's place, and we also try to get him to match his name to his photograph, to increase the chances of his recognising himself. We also ask parents to send in family photographs to help the child become more aware of those closest to him. The whole process is very slow and requires infinite patience. Every member of staff involved with the child puts him through the same paces to reduce or remove the possibility of dependence on one adult.

Dressing is an extremely complex business to get over to a child. There is a good chance that, wherever the child was before he came to us, there were not enough people involved to be able to spend the time needed to teach him to dress himself. It would be grossly unfair to criticise a mother who did not spend a lot of time trying to teach her sometimes exceedingly difficult and unco-operative, non-communicating child to learn how to dress. It is a long, slow process with any child; Mum has other things to do as well, and the quickest way to get something done is to do it yourself. Most of our children have no idea at all about dressing themselves when they first arrive, and the commonest response we receive when we try to get involved is a temper tantrum.

Once the child has realised that he is totally and utterly wasting his time in losing his temper every time someone tries to break into his little world, it is then possible to start to teach him the intricacies of putting his clothes on.

Like all other skills, this, too, is not a one-off session. It can be a very long drawn-out affair that may take many, many hours of patient teaching. A very useful tool is a system known as 'reverse chaining', which involves getting the child to put the finishing touches to a task which the teacher has almost completed. For example, if the child is being taught to put on his sweater, the teacher puts it on the child completely, apart from leaving him to put his arm through the second sleeve. Once he has mastered this technique, he is praised liberally and the session ends on a success note, which is vital at every stage. The next session starts with a repeat of the first, but this time the whole second sleeve is left for the child to finish off. Success is followed by praise again and the next lesson goes back another step. So it goes on each time, with the teacher hopefully doing less and the child achieving more and more. Some children will pick it up more quickly than others. The whole pace of the scheme has to be dictated by the teacher, using her knowledge of the child, her perception to know just how much the child can take at one sitting, and her experience to tell if the child has genuinely acquired the skill or not, and, if he is getting worked up, whether he has really had enough or is simply 'trying it on'.

As I have said frequently, a high staff-to-pupil ratio is very necessary for each child to be given the individual tuition he desperately needs if he is to be able to make progress. There is no chance at all of his being able to develop fundamental living skills if he is in a large class and only receiving sporadic individual attention from his teacher. All learning for the autistic child has to be intensive, prolonged and repeated many times if he is to succeed. It is also very important to keep quite detailed records of failures and successes, so that the child's progress, or lack of it, can be closely monitored and the way in which his problems are tackled can be altered, if need be, to best suit the individual child's needs.

Every skill which we try to impart must involve the use

of language. For example, imagine trying to teach a child to make a cup of coffee. We all take it for granted that it is very easy, but the following list indicates all the stages of this particular skill:

1 Unplug kettle
2 Take the lid off
3 Put kettle under tap
4 Turn tap on
5 Fill kettle up
6 Turn tap off
7 Return to plug
8 Plug in
9 Switch on
10 Boil kettle
11 Find cup
12 Find teaspoon
13 Add coffee
14 Add sweetener
15 Add boiling water
16 Add milk
17 Stir and clear up

From this task analysis it can be seen that the simple operation of making coffee is, in fact, extremely complex and every single step must involve the use of language, the ability to memorise sequences and the ability to co-operate. For a child who has precious little language and whose comprehension level is unknown, this simple skill becomes a mammoth task that can take literally months to impart, whereas most of us perform it several times a day without thinking about it.

In such a situation, the teacher has to keep detailed records on a previously prepared list, and mark off each stage as the child achieves it. She may also find that she has to go back regularly to reinforce various stages and may also have to contend with the child's temper and frustration.

It often appears that a child's level of normality is determined by his progress in the three Rs, and these subjects are often pushed hard. But I cannot agree that the teaching of these skills is of major importance. They are certainly useful but if, and only if, the child is able to use them meaningfully. However, it is all too common to see a child counting objects by rote and not having a clue what he is doing, or spending literally hours copying out reams of meaningless nonsense, or reading out huge chunks of literature without any apparent awareness of its meaning or relevance. I very recently saw an eighteen-year-old, functionally mute, autistic girl copying from a book on diesel engines: 'The D79 has twin bogeys at the front, a power output of 15,000 brake horse . . .' If only someone could give a valid reason for wasting the young lady's time in this ridiculous fashion.

If we have any child who we feel is capable of such academic skills, we try to encourage them, but we try to keep the work as closely related to reality as possible. Writing exercises, for example, consist of recording the day, the date, the day's menu, the things that have just happened in the child's life or the activities he has enjoyed doing. Number work is kept to relevant things, such as counting the number of cups needed for morning drinks or the number of children requiring a biscuit. Emphasis is placed on the teaching of a social vocabulary so that the child may perhaps learn the meaning of words such as 'toilet', 'open', 'closed', 'danger' and 'stop'. Obviously, if the child is capable of reading and writing just for the pleasure to be derived therein, he is encouraged to do so, but tabs are kept very carefully to make sure that it is a useful exercise and not developing into a jumble of nonsense or even an obsession.

Whatever we try to teach our children, we have to ensure that it is not simply going to turn them into a conveyor belt on which they are going to travel, churning out useless goods and data in the same way as a badly-programmed computer. We aim to teach useful skills, which we hope will make them more independent, and certainly those which will help them to meet the demands of a normal society. We have to try to concentrate on behaviour control, self-care skills (which involve washing, bathing, dressing, feeding and toileting) and also what we call community living skills, such as table setting, washing up, doing the laundry, cleaning the home, helping in the garden and generally learning to be tidy—all things that we would wish of any child.

The teaching of any skill should, if possible, be imparted in the relevant situation. If an autistic child has difficulty in generalising, what is the point of teaching him to wash up in a bowl on his classroom table when he can have a washing-up session in the kitchen? If he is to be taught how to make his bed, there is little point in teaching such a skill in the middle of the afternoon, when most people make their beds in the morning as soon as they get up. If the child is having a lesson about teeth cleaning, it is obviously better to teach him in the bathroom where we normally do such things. Money matters are very difficult to convey to a child, so why not take him to the shop to teach him with real money, rather than spend hours working with plastic coins? To achieve all this goes back to the original statement about high staffing levels. It is obviously impossible to achieve the above with a large group of children and one teacher, because our children do not learn very quickly and much time is needed to get anywhere. If the night staff are working on bed-making and their shift is over, the early staff complete the teaching session before breakfast. If a child is having difficulty dressing himself, the night staff know that they can leave him for the early shift and also know that his dressing will not be done for him. Should the child need more time, the member of staff who takes over can stay with him, leaving enough of her colleagues to supervise the other children through breakfast.

All our children have cookery lessons; there is only one place to do them and that is in the kitchen. I can see little point in sitting the child in the classroom rolling out pastry or mixing a cake, if he can do it in the kitchen so that he can see the places where things belong; he is also much more likely to hear the vocabulary of the kitchen, by having the chance to hear the names of 'kitchen things' as other children are being taught the same skills by other members of staff. Perhaps most importantly, he can learn to feel the atmosphere of the place as he works, and maybe learn more easily the concept of 'kitchens' and what they are for.

Art and craft are not so much subjects to be learnt as activities to be enjoyed. The idea with such lessons is to let the child derive pleasure from the activities and to experience the textures of clay, the pleasures of colours, the feel of different materials and the taste of paint and glue. In an incidental way craft lessons, although appearing to be free and easy, can be used for developing various other abilities, such as fine finger control for cutting, hand/eye co-ordination for placing this bit of clay here or that bit of glue there. He can continue to develop his ability to co-operate, he can see other children doing the same things and he can learn the rudiments of sharing and even working together with other children. A by-product could also be that some children might even develop some idea of the passage of time by learning that they have to wait for something to dry or to see pottery coming out of the kiln.

In every single activity that we engage in with the children, a very important factor is the development of relationships. This is greatly helped by the teacher placing herself in close proximity to the child so that he accepts her presence. All staff need to be sympathetic to the child's needs; they need to be perceptive enough to know how far to go in any given instance, and they need to display an aura of confidence to the child. This is best transmitted by the teacher having total confidence in her own abilities, which is why, when I see a staff member demonstrate a certain skill, I encourage her to volunteer to plan activities in that field, so that we have finished up with different people 'in charge' of cookery, art, music, gardening and horse riding. This person then loosely takes control of sessions in her own interests with several children and staff, so that it is not unusual to see, for example, the girl in charge of gardening spontaneously arrange a trip in the mini-bus to the local garden centre to buy plants. A visit to the local café on the way back is also a very useful experience for the children.

The girl who takes charge of horse riding, which we have found to be extremely therapeutic for the children, has often detoured to the garden centre near the stables to let the children see the goats and Charlie parrot—about whom Thomas could not stop talking. When the children ride for the first time most of them are absolutely terrified, but once they become used to it, the pleasure they can get is quite amazing. Their balance is improved, they seem to smile profusely and we find it is an excellent way to get language from some of them. For example, if a child who can say 'more' or sign it, wants a repeat of a trot or a jump, he has to speak or sign before he gets what he wants. We have also seen several examples of children who are frightened actually speaking spontaneously by being alarmed or upset. One child demanded, 'Want to get off, it's not fair', the first time she was plonked on a pony's back. This was the first time she had ever been heard to speak, apart from parroting things she had heard.

One of the most difficult things to teach is the acquisition of language. Since many speaking autistic children tend to latch onto the echoing stage of language and thus finish up with plenty of speech and no language, as a parrot learns speech which has no meaning, it is very easy to get sounds from the child before you realise that it has no valid meaning and that he is churning out a series of sounds which, to him, have no value at all. This is why we steer clear of speech therapy in the old-fashioned sense of the word. At one time, speech therapy was used to correct poor diction and articulation, and we have seen several children who fell victim to this approach. They articulate beautifully, stressing the terminal sounds of words and, in many cases, have no idea what they are saying.

The modern approach to speech therapy is totally different and the therapy would be much more accepted if its name was changed to describe what it really is—communication therapy. The idea now is to stimulate the child to communicate properly, in a meaningful way, and the days of 'How now, brown cow' are thankfully long gone. We have been offered the services of the local Speech Therapy Clinic, but the problem is that they can only offer a few sessions a week at the most. Our children need constant stimulation, but first they have to know the person working with them and this relationship takes a tremendously long time to establish before the child develops the confidence even to try to sort out his useful language—if, indeed, he ever begins to do so. We accept that most of our children will remain functionally mute, but this does not deter us from battling on regardless. Our whole day is centred around communication therapy, from the moment the children get up until they go back to bed. Everything we do, we try to make relevant to day-to-day living. We never read tales about talking animals or fairy stories, because we feel the children have enough to cope with in real life without getting involved in fantasy worlds.

Holidays we have had with the children have been, so far as we can tell, a resounding success. We have been away three times and each time the children have been exposed to new experiences and new environments, with new people to meet and strange, unusual things to do. We have found that my philosophy on changing routines frequently has paid off. The children, in the main, have been quite happy to go away from home and school for a week, and the few children who have learnt a reasonable amount of real language have been full of it when they have returned from the holiday. I have a beautiful picture on my office wall which Alexander asked spontaneously to be allowed to draw as soon as he returned from a holiday in Buckinghamshire, which included a trip to Woburn Abbey.

Whatever we try to teach our children, and whatever experiences we give them, it all takes a very long time to percolate. We can never be certain that we are actually getting through, but we have to continue to try, and the fond hope is that we are gradually nudging the children towards some level of normality.

11
THE PARENTS SPEAK

I once read a poem entitled 'Autistic Child so Fair of Face'. I cannot remember how it goes on, and substituted my own second line—'Your social standards are a bloody disgrace'. Yes, our children look beautiful; yes, they look incredibly normal, but they are a burden for families, who, as well as having to cope with a child with few or no social graces and no ability to communicate and lacking apparent awareness of his peers, his family or his environment, receive no sympathy from the public, because there is no apparent handicap, apart from the fact that the parents seem to be responsible for failing to sort out their offspring.

Whatever the problems or horrors we as teachers have to face in a working day, there is always the consolation that we can escape to our own homes, our own world, at the end of it and return refreshed the next day.

The parents of our children can never abdicate their responsibility in this way. All I can say is, 'God help them.' I shall never understand where they find the strength and courage to keep on against all the problems they face. The amazing thing is that so few families split up. Occasionally it happens, but most seem to stick it out and they have our total admiration.

It is a shock to any parent to be told that his or her child is handicapped. With an autistic child it must be even worse. With an obvious handicap the parents can see immediately that the child has a disorder but with our children the child appears normal at first and then the parents have to try to come to terms with the disastrous news that their perfectly normal-looking child has a devastating handicap.

GPs are often less than helpful in diagnosing the problem. The parents know that there is something wrong with their child and their concern and worry build to unbearable levels while doctors and other authorities dither and churn out the jargon. All the time parents are being judged by the behaviour of their child and they are often attacked, verbally, by outsiders; even the bravest and most determined are reduced to the appalling level of wanting to lock away and hide the offending child from public view. Life-long friends are lost; baby-sitters refuse to visit, at any price. The parents are caught in a nightmare spiral and it is often a sort of relief for them to find out that there is a name to their child's affliction and that other parents are going through the same torment.

Unfortunately, there are no recognised education programmes for parents. They are often left to cope with a disaster on their own, with varying degrees of success. The temptation is always there to give in, to find any way at all that will give some respite from the screaming, the self-mutilation and the complete lack of communication that are apparent in so many of these children.

It must be realised that it is the job of a school like Doucecroft to relieve this pressure on parents. They must be given the strength to want to cope with their child's problems and to help continue the improvements, however small, achieved by the school. This is by no means an easy task for the family. At Doucecroft we have shifts to cover the whole twenty-four hour day. Staff can change from one child to another to spread the load of difficulties and to bring a fresh brain to the problem of finding new solutions. Once a viable solution is found, successive staff can patiently reinforce its effectiveness without being dulled by over-exposure to the child's resistance. The parents have no such respite. They cannot be blamed for any regression because they have no relief night shift and cannot go away after a day with the child as we can. They cannot pass the child on to colleagues and get their breath back. Our holidays become their hell, our free time can become their misery time.

To understand the pressures that the parents and siblings are under, I asked them to write down for me how having an autistic child affects them. It makes heart-breaking reading, but it also underlines several common factors: the difficulty of getting an early diagnosis; the lack of support from the authorities; the sometimes hurtful attitude of the general public; the fear of what the future will hold for the child, especially when the parents are dead.

HURT- for family

* * *

Christopher's Mother

'It's not the end of the world.' When Christopher was first diagnosed as autistic we felt the bottom had fallen out of our world. What had we done to deserve this cruel blow? The effect it would have on our lives could only be detrimental—we thought. *Not true.* Like most parents of handicapped children we cried, argued, blamed ourselves for what had happened and then we talked. We decided that Christopher would fit in with our family life and that no allowances would be made for his handicap, which sounds cruel. *Not true.*

Christopher had always been a lazy baby—he did not crawl until he was fifteen months old and he was well over two before he walked. He would sit for hours screaming, flapping and banging his head against the wall. His behaviour was often embarrassing, particularly when out shopping and at other people's houses.

When Christopher was twenty-one months old our other child, Kirsty, was born. From that moment on Christopher was hateful to her. He lost no opportunity to hit or poke her, but then jealousy is not uncommon in this situation.

Christopher did not relate to us in any way, shape or form; he did not feel pain and did not appear even to recognise us. I think this was the most painful part. We felt so unloved. Nevertheless, we were determined that this situation would alter and so we set to work.

The Local Authorities put us on the waiting list for a peripatetic teacher. We waited for a number of months but in the end one visited us, one morning per fortnight. She tried to teach basic activities such as stacking bricks, sorting shapes and picture matching, all of which were tremendous feats for him since he would scream, kick and fight even at the mention of work. After a while he got used to these visits and 'homework' would be set in her absence. We would be given a task to work on and with the brief training I had been given by the teacher we attempted daily work sessions. We had to be very physical with Christopher, often gripping his hands around the object we wanted him to concentrate on—we always, always ended the work session on success. When Kirsty was old enough she would join in the sessions with us so that she did not lose out on our attention. It was a treat to see how a normal child attempted problems that were so difficult for Christopher.

We managed to get Christopher into the children's centre run by Southend Hospital. It was for children with all sorts of mental and physical handicaps. He attended two afternoons a week and gave me the break I badly needed. It also afforded me the opportunity of giving Kirsty a little bit more attention that she had had before.

I no longer felt so alone in the problem (I say 'I' because Philip, my husband, was at work all day and very often came home late), but I still often felt isolated at home and unable to cope. Christopher had a progress book which recorded the events that took place at the Children's Centre. I would do my best in the work sessions that took place at home to link in with the things that happened in the Centre. For a long time Christopher was unco-operative, uncommunicative and so desperately unhappy. He often regressed and slept terribly badly. We were lucky if we had one night's sleep a week. He would wake in the night screaming and screaming and there was nothing that would pacify him. We made a vow that he would never sleep in our bed and it often meant long vigils by his bedside until he settled down.

The specialist he was under at Southend prescribed medication to regulate his sleep patterns. It did not help at all. In the end we used to let him scream it out of his system. It seemed hard, but there was no way we could function in the day if we could not sleep at night. I lost so much weight in such a short time that my own health became a very real worry to us. The problem seemed to worsen when he transferred from a cot to a bed. We put a safety gate at his bedroom door and he seemed to associate this with the bars on his cot. For nearly two years he would not sleep in a bed. He would lie on a pillow on the floor by the gate—at least he should have a nice straight back!

When Christopher was four we managed to get him into the Doucecroft School for Autistic Children. The nursery staff visited us at home before he started and we explained the problems he had with sleeping. They showed us that we were reinforcing the unacceptable behaviour by allowing him to continue sleeping on the floor (we had been supplying him with pillows and blankets). They said we had to make a stand because otherwise he would still be sleeping on the floor when he was fifteen! We were advised to remove the gate completely and every time he got out of bed we had to march him back, with a slap if we felt it to be necessary. He had to be made to see that a bed was for sleeping in. That night we tried the theory out. My husband held Christopher down in his bed until he stopped screaming. Every time he got out of bed he was marched back, often with a smack. The next night we stood outside the door. As soon as he thought we had gone he got up. Back he was marched. After we had 'camped out' on the stairs for a

few nights he began to stay in bed. Now he will go u
to his room and 'play'; when he is tired he will crawl into
bed and tuck himself up.

Eating was an enormous problem to us. When Christopher was very small, getting him to feed himself was a work of art. Mealtimes were absolutely dreadful. Again we had to be very physical, wrap a hand around his and put him through the motions of feeding himself. After months and months we achieved success. Then a new problem cropped up—he became very fussy about food. He would only eat food which had gravy on it. He would eat food that was too hot. We tried to get him to blow on his food to cool it, but he would put the spoon to his mouth, say, 'Blow', put the food in his mouth and still burn himself. He began to lose weight because he was not eating. Most children will at least pick at things they like but Christopher did not seem to like anything. His bowel movements began to get less and less frequent; we were lucky if he went once a week and then he only performed if we held him down on the toilet. It seemed that every time we saw him we were getting at him in one way or another.

The school had similar problems. He refused to eat or drink at first, which was extremely worrying for us. Then the staff at the school decided he had to be made to eat. They hated doing it, but spoon upon spoonful were pushed into his mouth: he hated it and very rapidly began to feed himself. They sprinkled bran on his food to encourage his bowel movements.

The breakthrough came when he was invited to spend a week's holiday with the other children from the school at Great Yarmouth. We were very anxious at the prospect, but the other parents of the little ones had agreed that their children could go, so we gave it a try. On the holiday Christopher did not stop eating. He went to the toilet every day and when he returned to us that weekend he was lively, happy and visibly healthier than he had been for a long, long time.

tinued to eat well both at school and at home
e personality seems to have changed for the
full of fun, plays well with Kirsty, often
e play, and he chatters constantly. A lot of
hard to understand but he is beginning to
ulate his words well.

We have had a lot of problems over Christopher's short life. Many we have overcome, but we have had to fight with him and for him every step of the way. I cannot stress enough to parents how important it is to face the problems an autistic child poses. Do not skirt around it or compromise, however hard it might be. We are beginning to enjoy our life with Christopher, although he is far behind his sister. But it does not matter because we are going in the right direction and for the first time in four years we are beginning to look forward to the challenges that face us. With the backing, care and love showered on Christopher by his school and our family we will get there in the end.

Alex's Mother

Having a handicapped child is a tragedy, something you never really come to terms with. When you have what you think is a normal, healthy and really beautiful baby, then find out, at the age of four years, that he is autistic, that is a cruel blow. Firstly, the word in meaningless—I had never even heard it mentioned before.

Friends are very good and sympathetic but they cannot really understand what it is like. You cannot help feeling different from other people. When you meet new people and the inevitable questions come up about your family and you have to try to explain the situation, you cannot help noticing a pulling back of people. They do not know what to say and it builds a barrier between you.

An autistic child is an unknown quantity, a totally perplexing individual. It is very difficult to live with such a child, not knowing if something is going to upset him or if you are going to do or say something wrong. That child is a master at getting you wound up, starting over the most trivial thing until you explode and start screaming and shouting, then feeling so guilty that you cannot take the onslaught.

What would we do without Doucecroft, where people are dedicated to trying to help our children make more sense of life, to make them more aware of what is going on around them? When people ask how Alex is getting on I always find myself saying, 'He's doing fine', and painting a good picture, and in fact he is progressing. But there are times I wake up in the night and I know he is a handicapped child and he is not going to be able to cope with life on his own and I am scared. What does the future hold for him?

Jimmy's Mother

When Jimmy was a toddler his behaviour was terrible. He had tantrums when he screamed a lot and was hard to control. He would do this when taken out somewhere he did not like—clinics, shops, etc.—and sometimes at home if something unknown upset him. He showed no affection or recognition, never cuddled or kissed or pointed to things or did things that normal toddlers do.

At this stage we did not know that he was autistic, just very strange. People said he would learn to talk soon, he was just a late developer. He could not do anything for himself, had to be fed, stayed in nappies, showed no interest in trying to put on clothes or shoes like the other toddlers we knew. The doctor at the local clinic sent us to a hospital in London when Jimmy was about two and a half; they thought he was deaf. When he was about three and a half we saw another London doctor who, after a few minutes with us, said it was obvious that Jimmy was autistic. Seeing our shock, he asked if no one had suggested it before; we said they had not. We asked if he wanted to see Jimmy again; he said he did not. So we were left with this awful confirmation that he was a handicapped child and we did not know what to do about it.

Jimmy's Father

For a while Jimmy was at a local assessment centre for educationally subnormal children. It was about this time in his life that his behaviour was at its worst. It was eerie because he would sit for hours just gazing at his fingers or at a matchstick, which was something he had an obsession about. He would just turn the match over in his hands for hours, and at other times he would have violent temper tantrums which were completely uncontrollable. He did not actually seek to destroy things; he would just yell and scream and we simply did not know what to do about it. We tried to pacify him but most of the time it meant waiting for the storm to pass.

Most of these tantrums seemed to occur if we had gone out. People stared, which of course made us all the more embarrassed, and we made frantic efforts to calm him down. These either had no effect at all or even served to make him worse.

If we went out to friends, we would have to explain that his behaviour was bizarre and unusual and they used to be goodnatured and laugh it off, and most of them treated Jimmy quite well. It was only later, as he got older, that people found him a bit unnerving. They actually backed away from him and seemed uncomfortable with him around. Funnily enough, children seemed to accept him quite well, some of them very well indeed.

We could not really indulge in a lot of things other people did. We could not go anywhere that was crowded. We always liked to go for long drives, but we could never stay in bed and breakfast places because landladies just did not want people like Jimmy around. I am not blaming them, but it was very restricting for us as a family.

A big problem as he gets older is that his odd behaviour becomes more noticeable. You find yourself constantly apologising for the lad's existence. It is peculiar, it seems to evoke two different responses in me to people's comments when they find his odd behaviour offensive in some way. I sometimes have the urge to be offensive back; the other half of the time is spent explaining to them, 'Oh, he's handicapped', and, though not in words, imploring them to understand and be tolerant, and then I am apologising for my own son's existence again. I do not know why I should, but some people can be so dreadful. They openly stare at you—that is just one thing. You get remarks like, 'Can't you control that child?' and it is all very well coming back with a swift riposte, but you know the self-same thing is going to happen time and time again and you cannot answer back to the whole population of the earth.

I know it is often said that there is always someone worse off than yourself, and he could be worse than he is. Well, agreed, he could. In his own way he seems quite happy a lot of the time. He is a nice kid, he has some endearing ways. I do not know why they are endearing in particular, I suppose it is because we are his parents. I mean, we still have our parental affection for him, but unfortunately you tend to look very much on the black side of things for the future. Instead of thinking of everything he has achieved, you find yourself thinking more and more about what on earth is going to happen to him when he gets older, when you have got someone of seventeen or twenty. Is he going to be any better? Is he going to be that step nearer to what we think of as normality? Or is he going to be no better than he is now and so be all the worse for us? And you wonder what is going to become of him and of us. We do not know if he is going to develop any more disturbed behaviour patterns.

During the time Jimmy has been at Doucecroft, his behaviour has improved immeasurably; tantrums are virtually unknown and he has lost his obsessional behaviour patterns. There are a lot of things he can do for himself and his ability to care for himself has improved a great deal. If he remains placid and compliant, as he is most of the time now, there will not be many problems. But, as we get older, what will it be like? Will he be disturbed? We do not want to lock him up in some place or other, we want him here with us. But all the time it is so very, very worrying.

Another worrying aspect is the effect it is going to have on our other two children, both younger. I am personally of the opinion that there may be a silver lining here somewhere, because they do have to be quite tolerant and indulgent with him. They are both fully aware that there is something wrong with their big brother but in many ways they have not had a normal life. Perhaps it will be easier for them having been brought up with it; maybe they will be more tolerant and understanding of other people, having had a brother like this; I just really do not know.

Of course there is no point in feeling sorry for ourselves and in feeling depressed. We laugh and joke about him to other people. I think, perhaps, they get the impression that we are not worried and that we are quite happy to let him plod on in his own way while we enjoy life, but I think you tend to mask your true feelings because there is always the worry nagging and gnawing at you. It is like something eroding you. I guess some people find renewed strength from this sort of thing, when they have a purpose in life. They see it as their personal crusade and this is very commendable. I often wish I could feel the same way, actually, but no—you get the feeling that this is blinding yourself to the real hard facts. Poor old Jim—it is not his fault.

Richard's Parents

Our problems with Richard began in the Autumn of 1974 when, at the age of two years and nine months, he had what was diagnosed as a severe mystery virus. Three years later a paediatrician, hearing the symptoms of that illness, thought that Richard had suffered from meningitis which, he believed, could possibly cause a child to become autistic. The four years following that illness were extremely difficult and stressful—in fact, looking back on that time, I think it is a miracle that we survived at all as a family unit.

Richard lost all his language and almost constantly made a high-pitched squealing noise. He became particularly distressed if anyone called at the house; he would rush upstairs and throw anything he could lay his hands on. His sleeping patterns became extremely erratic as he would wake up in the night and stay awake for as long as five hours. During this time he would sob; it was a heartrending sound, but if we tried to comfort him he became more distressed than ever. He shrank from all physical contact and so it was impossible to have a loving relationship with him and this was the hardest to bear. The only thing that gave him any pleasure was an extremely vigorous 'acrobatic' session, including lots of bouncing on a bed; so many afternoons were spent in that way just to stop the screaming and the squealing. Apart from that one activity, he was totally uninterested in everyone and everything and needed help with all self-help skills.

So, life was very grim for the first four years. I felt so isolated for obvious reasons, I had hardly any contact with friends. My husband did all the shopping because I just could not stand the embarrassment of taking Richard to the shops because of the critical looks of passers-by. What made it even worse was that Richard had no 'label' during this time, so we had no excuse for his terrible behaviour. We had been referred to a child psychologist a few months after the illness and saw her at regular intervals for three years, only to be told that Richard was suffering from severe sibling regression, which just made us feel total failures as parents. We had no support whatsoever from either health visitors or social workers, not even a 'phone call, never mind a visit. After a lot of hassle we eventually got an appointment with a paediatrician.

Eventually, in March 1978, we arrived at the Maudsley Hospital. We were there five hours and it was almost with relief, after three years of getting nowhere, that we accepted the diagnosis that Richard was definitely autistic. During the next few months we had two more hospital visits, one to Great Ormond Street and one to the Royal ENT Hospital where they wanted to see if Richard was deaf. This involved an overnight stay (an experience never to be forgotten!) and two further trips, to the Nuffield Centre, which are stories in themselves.

The story so far has been very negative, but the turning point came in November 1978, when finally, at the age of six years and eleven months, Richard started to attend the Doucecroft School in Kelvedon, Colchester, 29 miles from home. In the years that Richard has been going there, he has changed from an extremely disturbed unhappy and withdrawn child with no language, who could do nothing for himself, to a happy and loving child who has some language and who can dress, wash and feed himself with confidence.

We do appreciate the hard work that has resulted in these changes and shall always be grateful for his place at Doucecroft. We feel sure that he is happy now and thoroughly enjoys his life at school and at home. He is certainly a much loved member of our family who now brings us much pleasure, and the love and kindness shown to him by his younger brother is really very moving to see. It is something that many friends have commented on. We feel that as a family we have been taught many valuable lessons through the experience of having an autistic child. Our sense of values has certainly changed and I think we have learnt what is important and what really matters. I also feel that Richard has brought an extra dimension into our lives. Maybe it is one of the paradoxes of life that through problems we really discover things that really matter. Of course, there is always a negative side; to deny that would be burying one's head in the sand, but we are thankful for what our experiences have taught us and I am sure that we shall go on learning for the rest of our lives.

David's Parents

David took a long time to be born and when he did finally manage it he was bluish. The nurses put him in an incubator for a few hours and then he was returned to me a normal colour. I felt right from the beginning that he was not right, but of course nobody would listen. He cried all day long but thankfully he was quiet at night.

He had an enormous appetite and seemed to develop normally apart from language and communication. We tried telling health visitors that David was not right, but all we got was that we were over-anxious and that he was a 'lovely baby'. It was like banging our heads on a brick wall. Finally, when David was about three, we had an appointment at Great Ormond Street because they thought an audiology test was needed to check for deafness. The audiologist gave him five hearing tests and it was he who first gave us the idea that David might be autistic; this was the first time we had ever heard the word. The hospital wanted him to be seen by the psychiatric unit but at the time he was pretty ill with tonsillitis and ear infections. He was admitted to hospital for an ear operation and a tonsillectomy, so we were busy worrying about that. After the operation he seemed more attentive and we thought that perhaps he would pick up and make progress. However, he was still extremely difficult to handle and by this time he had mastered the art of rocking, which nearly drove us mad.

By now the whole thing was driving us crazy and, after a lot of pleading with the Council, David was placed in a day nursery. We felt that this might help him to communicate better, being with other children, but it did not make an ounce of difference as he just shut himself off and rocked. He remained there until he was six and was then transferred to the assessment centre at the local school for educationally subnormal children. He did not make any progress there either, and so he was sent to a special school for autistic children, where he appeared to be happy and to make some progress. However, we were told after a year that he was not up to the school's academic standard! He was then placed in our Authority's one and only school for severely subnormal children, which had over one hundred pupils, and we felt that David was overwhelmed by the size and make-up of the school. Three years there and things really came to a head. David became progressively worse; he changed completely, his behaviour was intolerable, screaming, making himself vomit and throwing himself about. He became physically ill as well as mentally disturbed, so much so that he could not remain at home any longer. He was then taken into our Authority's short-stay unit for about three months and then we found out about Doucecroft at which a place was sought, offered and approved by our Education Department.

When David started at Doucecroft he became calm and manageable almost immediately. For the first time in thirteen years we felt that someone actually cared for our son as much as we did.

He has been at the school two years now and the improvement is fantastic. More than anything else, David is happy and settled.

Jane's Parents

Jane seemed quite normal for the first sixteen to eighteen months from birth, gurgling, crawling and walking at about fourteen months. Then something happened: it all went very quiet, she became very withdrawn and we knew something was not right.

After seeing many doctors, which seemed to take forever, we were told that Jane was mentally retarded/autistic/non-communicating—the sky fell in.

Why us? Why Jane? Had one of us upset Big G upstairs? Could there even be a God to let things like this happen to little children?

It is no use feeling sorry for yourself! You have to pick yourself up and get on with it. Life goes on, or so they say.

We try to treat Jane as a normal member of the family in every way possible, and I think we succeed as well as can be expected. Bradley, who is three years older than Jane, is coming to terms with the situation and loves his sister dearly. There is certainly no jealousy from Bradley when Jane is fussed, and he actually joins in. Strangely, there is a bit of 'green eye' when Bradley has a fuss made of him. We all love little Jane dearly.

Bradley used to sit and cry and ask why God cannot make her better; this is a very difficult one to explain if you do not have to walk away through the tears. Bradley was very much looking forward to having a baby sister; it has hit him hard.

To have a little girl like Jane causes many thoughts to cross your mind. You become very tolerant of some people but extremely intolerant of others; but then they deserve it. Our biggest cause of concern is how Jane will get on when we are not here any more. Although we are sure that Bradley would do his best, he has his own life to lead and we would not want him to be burdened.

Jane has made some progress while she has been at Doucecroft and gives us the most important thing—hope. Looking to the future, although we have that word 'hope', we are unable to think of things like Jane doing 'a bit of courting and sparking' and giving her away in marriage and her having a family.

Lots and lots of thoughts like these go through a parent's mind, as you can imagine. Is there a God?

Scott's Parents

Looking back now, I suppose we both thought that there was something wrong with Scott, compared with other children of his age.

I remember vividly taking Scott to tea with various girlfriends and, whereas their children, all born within weeks of Scott, were playing quite happily with different toys and with each other, Scott would just scream and scream and scream, so I had to take him home. This behaviour went on between the ages of six months and three years. We could not take him anywhere new or strange without tantrums and screaming fits. On his second birthday my sister had to take him out in his pushchair so that the other children could enjoy his party in peace.

Scott never crawled, just rolled about, but he was walking by his first birthday, albeit unsteadily. He ate reasonably well—the usual toddler food—and began to use a spoon and cup very well. His sleeping pattern was very erratic; from early on he hardly ever had the 'statutory' two hours in the mornings and afternoons. Always awake, it seemed. I spent hours tramping the streets with the pram in the hope that he would doze off—he did not. At night it became more and more difficult to get him off to sleep, so much so that every sedative was tried to achieve that aim, and the only one that worked was a herbal remedy. Soon the problem of getting him off was replaced by a worse one: he began to wake in the night and he refused to go back to sleep. We used to have to resort to locking him in his room and just let him scream himself to sleep. He used to shake his cot so much that it travelled the length of his room to his door so that he could try to get out. One morning I found him asleep in the wreckage of his cot because he had shaken it to pieces.

At two and a half Scott started at nursery school and it was soon discovered that he just would not conform. Having no language, just one monotonous sound, and having no idea of toilet-training, made matters very difficult for the staff. It was suggested that he was perhaps suffering from a hearing problem and that we ought to see a doctor. We knew positively that he could hear but went to see the doctor anyway, and from then on we started on our journey through the bureaucratic system in an endeavour to find the cause of our son's irrational and unpredictable behaviour. Around this time Scott went off normal food and survived solely on bananas, chip-sticks, Marmite, toast and Weetabix.

I do not know how many times we heard from our GP and the local Child Health Clinic, 'No need to worry, lots of children don't talk till they're five or six.' Next patient, please! Not to be fobbed off with all this, we pleaded with our doctor to get something done. Eventually speech therapy was suggested and that was a total waste of time, but every avenue had to be explored. We had heard from various quarters that the Nuffield Centre in London was a good place and so this was the next place we tried. After various attempts to get our GP to write (everything has to go through your GP) we finally got an appointment at the Nuffield at the end of April 1980. Around the same time we had a letter from an educational psychologist who must remain nameless. He produced a mammoth questionnaire and came to no conclusion at all. When we asked this 'expert' about special schooling, he muttered something about waiting lists and then said that our lad could not go on the list until he was three and a half—at the time Scott was three and a quarter.

At the Nuffield, after a strenuous day of tests and assessments, they came to the conclusion that there was nothing wrong with his hearing but there was definitely something wrong with him. They were not capable of saying what it was, so they referred him to the Maudsley Hospital, also in London. It was difficult to get an appointment there as well, because we had to go back to the GP and the educational psychologist again, to get them to submit independent reports. More red tape. The report was sent by the doctor promptly enough, but how many times can you 'phone an educational psychologist to get him to send off his report? It was the middle of July when I remember screaming down the 'phone at the 'expert' to do something. When this did not work, either, our GP suddenly came to life, and he rang the psychologist and told him to get his report off to the Maudsley *now, pronto!*

Finally, in September, Scott was diagnosed as autistic, and very much so, by the Maudsley Hospital. At last. We then had to wait for a space at the local assessment centre in Southend and Scott was finally admitted there in October 1980. Without our pushing he would be waiting still. The school did their best with him but could not do a lot. They did not have the staff to cope with him and everyone lost out. So we went back to asking for placement in a school for autistic children and finally Scott was offered a place at Doucecroft School in Kelvedon, near Colchester, nearly forty miles away. Since being there, Scott has changed from a horror to a delightful child. Gone are the severe hyperactivity, the unpredictability, the head-banging, the frustration and the outbursts of extreme temper. He is now far more calm in his demeanour, gets less cross if things go wrong and in general is far more disciplined.

We still get tantrums, but they are less frequent and are short-lived. Now that he has the beginnings of language development, he gets enjoyment from communicating with words. He still has his obsessions, however.

During the day, if the TV happens to be put on, he will draw all the curtains and bring down his duvet and sit close to the television with the duvet and pillows over him. At night he will not have any lamps on until the street lights come on and will sit watching the television in the dark. We dare not use the hose while he is around as he will not stop using it. He had an incurable desire to nip quickly and quietly upstairs when no one is looking, go into the bathroom and find something to tip out (shampoo, foam bath, toothpaste, after shave, perfume). We have the most beautiful-smelling carpets! Still, this is a phase that will pass and another will take over.

We are fortunate in that we have an understanding family and friends who will lend a hand with baby-sitting, etc. You always have to have someone who knows Scott's peculiar ways and who will not get upset if he has a tantrum.

* * *

All the above stories from my children's parents underline the pain and the struggle they have had to get help for their children. To parents of children not at Doucecroft I would give the following advice which falls into two categories. The first is about fighting for help for your child and the second is about helping yourselves. If you are convinced that your child is experiencing communication problems and possibly developing behaviour problems as well and, having read this book, feel that your child could be autistic, then seek help as soon as possible. Do not allow yourself to be fobbed off with comments like, 'he'll grow out of it'. If he is autistic he will not do so. The first step is to contact the School Psychological Service (SPS) at the local Child Guidance Clinic (CGC) and request an interview with an educational psychologist, and do not be deterred. You have a legal right to education for your child from the age of two to nineteen if his condition warrants it. You have read many instances in this chapter of parents being smothered in patronising jargon. Refuse to accept it and, if you get nowhere, start to make a fuss as firmly as you can, but do not become abusive because the people you are dealing with are trying to do a good job under a lot of pressure.

Helping yourselves by trying to sort out your child is not an easy job, but if you get involved with the child as early as possible you stand a chance of coming through and of keeping your sanity. The first thing that has to happen is that you must decide what limitations you plan to put on your child. Once established, these guide-lines need to be firmly, rigidly and consistently, repeat *consistently*, applied. Make a rule for yourself: if you are going to have a battle, make sure you plan to win; if you do not plan to win, do not even start the battle. The only way your child will ever learn is if he knows precisely where he stands. He must learn that his unacceptable negative actions will never, ever receive the accolade of his parents or anyone else, and on the other side of the coin he must also learn that anything he does right will always be rewarded. As I have gone to great lengths to explain, he must also be praised and rewarded for stopping doing something wrong.

If your child is developing a craving for obsessional routine, break it as often as you can. If he screams when you change your route to the shops, so be it; he will definitely take the change eventually, although you cannot expect overnight acceptance, but this will only come if you are very firm and exceptionally consistent. Mealtimes can be a nightmare unless you decide otherwise. Extremely firm handling is called for, but you will get there if you persevere. If you accept that it could take an hour or more to get one plateful down, and that it could be hell from start to finish, then have a go at it, but do not expect it to work first time. If your child will not sleep, try what Christopher's parents did, but, as with everything, do not start unless you plan to carry on until you win.

One mistake that many parents make is to rush things, especially if any signs of language appear, because it is the use of language that renders the child closest to normality. You need to accept the fact that your child may never speak, but that does not imply that he will never be able to communicate. If there are no signs of spoken language, find out about Makaton sign language or any other signing systems. Most headteachers of special schools would be pleased to help you out with pamphlets and booklets.

Do not give up, because if you do and the child begins to rule the roost at home, you may soon have an insurmountable problem which you will never survive. I cannot give specific details for programmes because I do not know your child, but if you feel the need, contact me. My staff and I may just be able to help:

Ian B. Ashton,
Doucecroft School,
163 High Street,
Kelvedon,
Colchester,
Essex.

Tel: (0376) 70060

12
NO STANDING STILL

Being in charge of an independent school has distinct advantages and disadvantages. The main points on the plus side are that I am not hamstrung by Local Authority red tape and, to a very large extent, I am completely autonomous. I am always responsible to my Board of Governors and am very fortunate in having a very good team to fall back on in times of crisis, especially on the few occasions that I have had to exclude a child. However, I am fortunate in that they tend to leave me and my staff to get on with running the school as we see fit. In spite of being independent, we are still closely scrutinised by the DES, which is a good thing; it means that Local Authorities have the backing of the State in sending children to us, and also it means that we cannot be called 'cowboys' because the DES is so keen on high standards, especially outside the State school system.

The independence also gives us a free hand to experiment in spheres which may need years of discussion in the State bureaucratic system. For example, I have long adhered to the theories of 'junk food' problems, so instead of having to consult dieticians and the like, we simply converted our children's diet to an additive-free one. The only cost incurred was the purchase of a book called *E for Additives*, which tells you the toxic effects, if any, of all permitted flavourings, colourings and preservatives. Many people said that 'junk-free' food, being scarcer, was dearer, but we have not found this to be the case. Wholefood margarine, for example, is only coppers more than plastic marge, but it is tastier and so you tend to use less. I am convinced that chemical food can cause hyperactivity in some children and some of ours are incredibly hyperactive. I have no actual evidence to prove that a change of diet prevents or reduces hyperactivity, but our children seem to be thriving on a more wholesome diet, some of the more disturbed ones seem calmer and, if nothing else, we are no longer making our possibly chemically damaged children absorb even more toxic rubbish.

Another big advantage for us is that we are not tied to a finance director's budget. We have an accountant who very generously charges not a penny for his services. He reports to meetings about the state of resources at any given time—if we need something and the money is there, we order it and get it with the minimum delay and without forms in triplicate. If we cannot afford it, we wait; we never buy anything without having the wherewithal first or without being able to guarantee its imminent arrival.

Over the years we have been able to introduce many changes and improvements. Many of these have been because they were vital, many because the children have improved so much. We now have our own potter who comes in to school on a consultancy basis each week. She is a professional and her skills are such that the children feel her confidence and respond beautifully. We have our own electric kiln, which was given to us by the First Years at a local Comprehensive School, and the pots the children produce are fantastic. When I look back over the years and see children concentrating for upwards of an hour on moulding clay with infinite patience, and realise that these are the very children who spent years in isolation and misery, I can honestly say that I am delighted with my job and would not swap for all the tea in China.

In the autumn of 1984 a chance comment by a colleague set me thinking about a new project for which to raise funds. She made an observation that many of our children seemed to be enjoying swimming so much more, and would it not be fantastic if we had our own pool? The general opinion was the same, so I approached the committee and put in a request for permission to have a pool. The trivial matter of the cash did not panic us because, even though we are just one charity sharing in the generosity of the public, we knew that if we had something for people to contribute to, we would soon raise the cash. At every lecture I did from then on for the next six months, I was able to tell people that we were aiming for a swimming pool and the money poured into the fund. The company chosen for the job started in spring 1985 and had it ready in eleven weeks flat. As they were finishing off the tiling, I happened to comment that, as I had raised the lion's share of the cost, what with all my begging letters and lectures, then they ought to put my name in tiles on the floor. This was said in a totally flippant manner, but when I went out two hours later they had put I.A. forever on the floor in blue. I was secretly pleased, knowing that in fifty years time someone would pass by and casually ask, 'Who's this I.A., then?' to which the answer would be 'Haven't a clue, mate!'

The pool is big enough for all the children and is heated. I wrote to all the parents and asked them to contribute £25 each towards the running costs for the season, which we reckoned would run from May through to the end of September. As soon as the pool was ready we sat back and waited for the summer to arrive. We had a total of five weeks' use from the pool, including the last two weeks of the term, in which it poured down. We put the children in regardless, because they were going to get wet anyway. In spite of the weather we feel the pool was worth every penny because of the confidence it inspires in the children and the pleasure they all seem to derive from it. Right through the winter, every playtime, Alexander stared forlornly over the fence and one day even asked if it was possible to swim with ice on the pool.

Early in 1986, we were all fed up with the hassle involved doing art and craft in the classrooms, especially as we were now into pottery, jewellery-making and basketry, as well as the usual painting and slopping around of glue and associated messes. I persuaded the committee of the tremendous therapeutic value of art, of the confidence it can inspire in children who hitherto have achieved next to nothing, and pointed out how limited this valuable work is without a real art room. To keep the peace and to prevent me from sulking, the committee agreed and told me the money needed raising first. The cash poured in even faster than it did for the pool and, before the builders began, we had all the money in hand, all £11,500 of it.

Once again the rounds of the planners began. You would have thought I was building a second Post Office Tower, the way they argued the slope of the roof, the type of materials, the finished colour of the rendering and even the verticality of the windows (which I agreed to alter without even knowing what it meant). After four months' delay we received permission, after which the next step was to knock down the old conservatory which stood on the site. To save the Society a few hundred pounds' worth of demolition costs, I did the job, along with one of the fathers and a friend. We had quite a laugh, as they are also north countrymen, we learned a few more 'Did you hear the one about?', and got the job done in three hours flat. The construction began in March 1986 and took about eleven weeks. Once the shell was finished I was able to get in to paint it and set up the units and shelving. It is a boon to have the kiln in a safe place and to have all the art equipment under one roof. Everyone is happy with the whole thing and the children can do their art in peace, without leaving a mess all over the classrooms.

The major disadvantage of working for a charity is that we are almost permanently dependent on public subscription, although each child's Local Authority pays us a set fee which is set at a level designed to meet basic running costs. If there is to be a large salary increase we have to raise the fees to cover it. There is also the perennial headache of inflation to consider, as we find costs spiralling all the time. Whilst the Authorities accept that costs must inevitably rise and therefore so must the fees, there is no way that they can be expected to subsidise extensions and alterations, repairs and renewals. Therefore it is down to us to raise the extra money we need from public subscription. This is usually quite easy, but people do not have bottomless pockets and a tremendous number of other charities are calling for their help. One of the most worthy causes ever, the Band Aid appeal, received millions, but we obviously suffered with a decline in donations. Having said that, we have been exceptionally well supported by a vast number of people, from Round Tables to churches, from Rotary and Lions to Cubs and Brownies, from Masonic Lodges to companies both large and small, with shops, schools, individuals, pensioners, anonymous donors and hundreds of others in between. Over the years we have built up a very good relationship with the press and they can always be relied on to turn up with a photographer for the smallest donation to be publicised, and to keep us in the public eye. Thousands of begging letters have also served their purpose.

The major source of our fund-raising has been the vast number of lectures I have given over the years. Eight hundred and fifty-four was the last count at the end of July 1986. I have to admit that it is now a chore to force my weary bones from the armchair, especially on a dank and dirty winter night, to drive perhaps thirty miles each way to talk to a group about my work and my children. Once I get there and into my stride I can survey the audience and decide which approach to take. I enjoy educating people about autism and sometimes, if they merit it, I revel in shaking them out of their complacency. I find it extremely rare to get no response and the majority of people have been shocked to realise that such children exist; the result is that we usually receive a healthy donation, either on the night or after they have organised a function prompted by my talk.

There have been a few disasters among the successes. I spoke to one particular group which has to remain anonymous. I was invited to speak one December night at a place some thirty-seven miles from home. I reckoned it was worth it when I was promised a fifty-plus audience. I crawled there in thick, freezing fog to find that this large audience was reduced to seven old dears. 'It's the weather you know, Mr Ashton,' said Madam Chairperson. I mumbled something about having spotted that myself on the way and set up the photographs, the video for a film and my giant whisky bottle which I always take with me for donations. Three members of the group were knitting and I fully expected them to stop as I began, but they did not. As I launched into my lecture the smoke poured from their needles and the distraction factor rating reached a peak. Eventually I looked at Madam Chairperson with pleading in my eyes and she got the message. Her 'ladies', with a stare and a glare over her half-moon spectacles, had the desired effect, but not until one of the doughty ladies came back with a very disgruntled, 'Well! It is a charity blanket, after all . . .' My great powers of perception at this moment told me that my cause was lost, so I struggled valiantly to the end and drove home in misery.

The school has always been very much a self-help organisation. A ramshackle garage, the gable end of which forms part of the playground boundary, was in a terrible state and quotations in the order of a thousand pounds for demolition and carting away prompted me to write to all the fathers to ask if any of them could offer enough intelligence to swing a pick and sledgehammer or wheel a barrow. They were also bribed with the possibility of a free fish and chip lunch and a can of beer. Apart from one meany who chickened out by catching a very severe dose of 'flu, every single father turned up, along with the local Boy Scout troop and their captain and the

Chairman of the Governors. I had conveniently forgotten to mention until they arrived that there were also two hundred and eighty-odd square yards of turf to be laid, because this demolition came up just after the swimming pool was finished and the garden had to be landscaped. We had a great day and I had plenty of opportunity to chat with some of the fathers as friends, and not just as the parents of our children. Everybody learned at least thirty new jokes and everything was completed by 5.00 p.m.

One dreadful day that I shall never forget was a Saturday in 1980. We had decided that the high cost and inconvenience of using oil had to come to an end, and so we planned to convert to gas. As usual, we did not have the money to pay outside contractors, so like a fool I volunteered to do it myself. By hand, I excavated a 75 foot trench, put the gas pipe in place, filled in the trench again, replaced the turf, went home, sat down, and had a heart attack. Six months later, I had three coronory arteries by-passed and had six weeks off work. Everybody was most solicitous after my well-being, but their concern was not needed to make me slow down. When you are only 34, you think you are invincible and that you can go on forever, but you cannot. It was a hard lesson to learn, but I certainly learned it. I no longer rush around like a demented lemming, I only do light jobs like knocking down conservatories to make space for art rooms, but even then I only did a bit, moving the same brick around all day, while the others grafted. It is in no small way due to my very reliable and lovely staff that I can now sit back a bit and see the fruits of our labours. But then I get bored and finish up having to think of even more ways of improving an already pretty good school.

When the school opened in 1977, we automatically inferred, without even mentioning it, that we would have to do something later about the future care of our children. The law states that a child is only entitled to education up to the age of nineteen years. After this, there is no law and the child is then dependent on arbitrary decisions made by the Social Services. It would be a crime to give a child several years of the good life and then to turn him out to be left to his own devices while, at the same time, his parents would be that much older and less able to cope. Some autistic children make the grade, but they are very few and far between, so if the child needs care for the rest of his life, he must be given such care. The National Society had reached the same decision and had started two or three centres which they called Life Care Centres. They took children from their schools, having persuaded the Social Services that it would be cheaper than leaving the children at home with daily attendance at Adult Training Centres, which would not be able to cope with them, much cheaper than psychiatric or subnormality hospitals and definitely much more cost-effective than psychiatric care for the parents once they cracked up under the pressure.

In 1982 we decided to start looking for a building that was suitable for our purpose and we went through the usual rounds of receiving all the rubbish under the sun from estate agents. We looked at several, then the Society repeated their act of faith with me by taking on a Principal to get the ball rolling. Alex Wallace and I scoured the countryside and chanced upon an old rectory which was in our price bracket. We took the plunge and persuaded the bank manager that the only thing he could do was loan us more money. He gently pointed out that we still owed money on the school, but soon relented when we showed him all the figures, and especially when we pointed out that we had made all our interest repayments on time. We bought the Old Rectory in 1983 and Alex set about persuading the Social Services of the value to be obtained in funding children there. We only had one child ready to leave there and then and, after much debating, Stewart was transferred. Some of the other places were taken up by children from other Authorities outside

Essex. Eighteen months later we were able to secure a place for Claire.

Unfortunately, Social Services nationally brought out a new set of guidelines which have effectively become rules. They said that residents in such places as ours had security of tenure, which meant there had to be a very good reason for exclusion after their first six months. This confounded our plans, because we had hoped to offer what could loosely be described as training courses for the non-Doucecroft children, who would then have to leave for other placement as soon as the next Doucecroft child was ready. Even without such rules to follow, we would still finish up with a place full of ex-Doucecroft children. Autistic children have a normal life span and, because the centre is for life care for those that need it, we already find ourselves with an embryonic, geriatric autistic community, so we already need to get ready for another centre for our next group of leavers. It is impossible to select children for the school on an age basis so that they could fit into a 'leaving pattern'; and so we may have one group of children ready to leave together, followed by a gap of a couple of years or so. Thus we have a perennial headache. We have children being put forward for the nursery because of the 1981 Education Act, but there is no room yet as our older children are still under nineteen and the problem is further complicated by the fact that the Social Services will not guarantee to fund leavers anyway.

The whole idea of the Old Rectory is to continue with the individual programmes from school and to expand them. Just as at Doucecroft, the emphasis there is on self-care and what can be loosely termed 'community living skills', because even with very limited communication skills, a resident in an adult centre needs to be able to look after himself and to cope with domestic chores such as cooking, washing up, making beds, and helping with the cleaning. The Old Rectory timetable has also been extended to cover gardening and animal care, leather work, copper work and restoration of old furniture. They also try their hand at pottery and their art room is a great success and a source of pleasure to several of the young people. The residents are in smaller rooms with only two beds, and they can go there for peace and quiet if they wish. There are plenty of chances for the more able young adults to go out to the shops alone if they wish and are able to do so. One or two of them go to the Post Office to collect their State allowance and have a good spend on the way back. They often go to the beach hut that they were given and have days out there. Without such a centre these young people would have had nowhere to go after the age of nineteen and, as their parents grew older, there would have been no choice for them apart from hospitals, which would be a crime.

Although the '81 Act is a blessing, it also creates problems. These children need help and we can give it if we have the places. The DES limits the size of the school to twenty-one and we are always full. What I should like to do is set up another school, but this time it would have to have very large grounds so that it could be expanded as and when children were ready to leave at nineteen, and they would then just move across the grounds to a Life Care Centre which could grow with numbers. Apart from the very trivial matter of the money, it would be a doddle. I know what sort of building to look for, I know exactly what would be needed in the way of equipment, I am on first name terms with the Education Officers, the Fire Officers, HM Inspectors, and I have become an expert in the fine art of persuading people to part with their money. So, all it needs is a quick word with the bank manager and away we go . . .